OTHER BOOKS BY ALAN MOORE

D.R. & QUINCH'S TOTALLY AWESOME GUIDE TO LIFE
HALO JONES BOOK ONE
HALO JONES BOOK TWO
HALO JONES BOOK THREE
SHOCKING FUTURES
SWAMP THING BOOK ONE
SWAMP THING BOOK TWO
SWAMP THING BOOK THREE
TWISTED TIMES
WATCHMEN

SWAMP THING VOLUME FOUR
ISBN 1 85286 017 0

Published by Titan Books Ltd,
58 St Giles High St,
London WC2H 8LH

First British edition: December 1987
10 9 8 7 6 5 4 3 2 1

Printed and bound in Great Britain by
Richard Clays, Chichester, W. Sussex.

Created by Len Wein and Berni Wrightson

Volume Four

Written by
ALAN MOORE

Pencilled by
STEPHEN BISSETTE
SHAWN McMANUS
RON RANDALL

Inked by
JOHN TOTLEBEN
SHAWN McMANUS

TITAN BOOKS

ALAN MOORE

Alan Moore began work as a cartoonist/illustrator in 1979, concentrating on comics scriptwriting in 1980. Contributions to Fleetway's *2000 AD Future Shock* series as well as scripts for Marvel UK's *Captain Britain* and *Dr Who Weekly* were followed by *Marvelman* and *V for Vendetta* in Quality's *Warrior*. In 1983 DC Comics commissioned him to write *Swamp Thing* and then *Watchmen*, now issued as a graphic novel by Titan Books in the UK. Also for DC, Alan has scripted *Killing Joke* for Brian Bolland to draw and a film script for Malcolm McLaren. He is a dominant scripting influence in contemporary comics.

STEVE BISSETTE

Inspired by the underground comic *Zap*, Steve Bissette collaborated on the fan comic *Abyss*, which he used to gain acceptance into Joe Kubert's School of Cartoon and Graphic Art. After graduating in 1979, his first professional work was for various DC Horror and War Comic books. This was followed by collaboration with John Totleben on *Bizarre Adventures* for Marvel Comics and *Swamp Thing* for DC Comics. He has completed *Godzilla* for Darkhorse Comics and he is currently developing projects with Mirage Studios.

JOHN TOTLEBEN

After a childhood in Erie, Pennsylvania, spent consuming a steady diet of comics, monster magazines and monster movies, John Totleben went to the Joe Kubert School of Cartoon and Graphic Art where he met Steve Bissette. Together they worked on *Bizarre Adventures*, followed by *Swamp Thing*, which they drew for almost three years. Currently, he is illustrating *Miracle Man* for Eclipse Comics and producing *Taboo* with Steve Bissette for Aardvark One International.

SHAWN McMANUS

Shawn attended the New England School of Art and Design. His interest in comics was touched off by the discovery of Berni Wrightson's work in the medium. In 1984 he moved to New York where an introduction to Len Wein led to jobs for DC Comics. Apart from his work on *Swamp Thing*, he has also drawn the *Green Arrow* back-up strip in *Detective Comics*, a *Legion of Superheroes* tale and *The Omega Men*. More recently he has been working in the field of animation from his home in Los Angeles.

RON RANDALL

Ron's interest in comics led him to enrol at Joe Kubert's School of Cartoon and Graphic Art in 1978. During the course he worked on back-up stories in *Sgt Rock* for DC Comics. After graduating in 1981 he drew a number of strips for DC including *Barren Earth, Warlord, Arak, Teen Titans* and the graphic novel *Me and Joe Priest*. While only drawing one issue of *Swamp Thing* he contributed to the inking chores on further issues. In 1987 Ron began work on *Airboy* for Eclipse Comics and created the science fiction series *Trekker* for Darkhorse Comics, both of which are his current projects.

INTRODUCTION

"Trifles Light as Air and Otherwise"

After three volumes of *Swamp Thing*, you might think you had a good idea of what to expect from the fourth. Appalling menaces to humanity come from Outside to wreak doom upon us. More Dark Messiahs, more demons, more Nightmares. And you'd be right.

And you'd be wrong. Mostly you'd be wrong. It's true that within these pages you will find the loneliest animal of all; and that some of the things the animal does menace humanity and the other living things on this planet. But in this book the darkess is on the inside, and it's worse for all that.

Book Four of *Swamp Thing* has much to do with love and dreams as it has to do with hate and destruction. As you will see.

It is easy to forget, seeing the *Swamp Thing* tales preserved in bound volumes for posterity, that this was not how they originally appeared. Like the vast majority of American comics they were produced monthly: month after month, twenty-three pages of *Swamp Thing* script were written by Alan Moore, laid out and pencilled by Steve Bissette and inked by John Totleben.

Any attempt to produce art on a schedule like that can run into problems. If an artist or a writer get behind then there are two alternatives; either one skimps, turns in a fast but less than competent job; or one completes what one is doing to the standard one is aiming for and risks blowing publication dates sky high, upsetting editors, losing work and so forth. The first two stories in *Swamp Thing* Book Four were both produced as fill-ins to prevent this happening.

The first, *Pog*, is my own personal favourite of all Alan Moore's *Swamp Thing* stories. It's a tribute to the work of American cartoonist Walt Kelly, and his creation, Pogo Possum. Kelly began working as a cartoonist for the Walt Disney Studios in the thirties. During World War Two he worked as a civilian employee for the army, producing artwork for language manuals. From 1948 to 1949 Kelly was art director at the short-lived but idealistic *New York Star*, for whom he revived an earlier character, Pogo, in the form of a daily comic strip. When the *Star* folded *Pogo* went into syndication and was highly successful. Kelly died in 1973 and the strip ended with him.

Pogo was one of the many inhabitants of the Okeefenokee Swamp, scene of many a strange tale and pointed political satire. Kelly was that unusual animal, a liberal, left-wing, American newspaper strip creator, who used the strip to discuss and parody such targets as the John Birch Society and the McCarthy hearings — at a time when almost all other American comic strips were most definitely right-wing.

For some time, Moore had wanted to do a tribute in which the swamp-dwelling Pogo met Swamp Thing. His chance came when he heard that Shawn McManus would be doing the art on *Swamp Thing* for an issue, while Bissette and Totleben recovered from the *Swamp Thing Annual, (Down amongst the Dead Men, Swamp Thing* Book Three) and began to work on *Swamp Thing 34, Rite of Spring*. Alan knew that McManus' cartoonier style would be ideal for the book, as indeed it was.

One of the many delights of *Pog* is in Moore's inventive use of language — what Humpty Dumpty referred to, in Lewis Carroll's *Through the Looking Glass*, as 'portmanteau words'; words such as *millenderings* which contains both 'millennia' and 'wanderings') or *guardiner* (with shades of 'gardening' and 'guardianship'). This hodge-podge language is a joy to read, a tribute to the peculiar dialect of Kelly's strip, while still being something uniquely Moore's. (As an aside, Alan maintains that once he had finished this strip, he found it difficult to write in normal English once more.)

Abandoned Houses is also a tribute, as well as being a 'fill-in' book. Because of the extra time needed by Steve Bissette to pencil *Rite of Spring* it became obvious that it would be late, and that *Swamp Thing 33* might have to be a reprint book. To prevent this Moore wrote *Abandoned Houses* for *Swamp Thing 33* in only a day, and Ron Randall turned in a creditable art job at short notice.

Full comprehension of the story, and of the two characters who inhabit its dreamscape, may require some rather esoteric background information. It has long been a tradition in comics (one that goes back at least as far as EC Comics' famous horror titles in the early fifties) to give horror anthology titles a host as a unifying theme. The host's function was to introduce the short stories, and occasionally to come into the last panel and make an appalling pun about the 'twist' ending, of the "Well, readers, Pierre the Hangman proved a real PAIN in the NECK!!" variety. DC's two main horror titles, *House of Secrets* and *House of Mystery*, were no exception. Their respective hosts were a fat, slightly terrified demon named Abel, and his thinner, worse-tempered brother, Cain.

It was in *House of Secrets*, in 1972, that the very first *Swamp Thing* story appeared — an eight page story that served as a try-out for the Wein-Wrightson series (and incidentally won the comics equivalent of an Oscar as best short story).

By the time that Alan Moore was writing *Swamp Thing*, both *House of Secrets* and *House of Mystery* had been cancelled and *Abandoned Houses* is on one level a tribute to both those comics and to their respective hosts.

Moore, had in 1984, been wondering how to incorporate that original *Swamp Thing* tale into the canon. With this story he got his opportunity, and he began to explore much of what later became important for *Swamp Thing*. Here is the real first sense we get of his role and lineage as an Earth Elemental. Here, too, is the first mention of the Trouble — the long and tortuous learning process that goes through in *American Gothic*, which will form Titan's *Swamp Thing* Books Five to Eight.

Moore also managed ambiguously to tie Cain and Abel into their Biblical namesakes. (Are they the original Cain and Abel? Or are they, as they variously claim, dreams or right-brain constructs?) This reveals in the process a darker side to the two horror hosts, while still allowing them to keep their fair share of secrets and mysteries.

Rite of Spring, *Swamp Thing 34*, was the vegetable sex issue, responsible for attracting more readers to *Swamp Thing* than any before. Moore wrote what was essentially a prose poem: a hallucinogenic consummation between a seven foot high mound of vegetation and an expatriate Balkan. Many consider it to be one of the high points of the series. The artwork, by Bissette and Totleben, is outstanding — perhaps their personal favourite on the series — although this was marred by the fact that the issue's cover was stolen from the DC mailroom.

The first part of *The Nukeface Papers* was written six months earlier, intended for *Swamp Thing 29*. Concerned that it might be too downbeat or too slow for the new readers that the book was attracting, editor Karen Berger suggested that it should be held off for a while. As it was, it fits perfectly as the prelude to *American Gothic*.

Nukeface was a character created by John Totleben and Steve Bissette as part of the try-out artwork they initially did in order to get work on *Swamp Thing*. As a victim, he is a commentary on the problems implicit in nuclear waste dumping; a representative of the nuclear industry, and its unacceptable face.

Nukeface's line at the beginning of the first story 'There's glory for you', is also a quote from Lewis Carroll's Humpty Dumpty — someone who felt, like Nukeface (and the nuclear industry?) that words can mean what you want them to mean — words in this case like 'safe'... Moore had earlier used 'The Glory' as a metaphor for nuclear fission in the first episode of *Marvelman* (aka *Miracleman* in the USA) in which he first began to explore the ramifications of superheroes in the real world.

The newspaper headlines and articles that litter the story, continually reminding us that behind the fiction there is a chilling reality, were collected by Moore, Bissette and Totleben in just two weeks.

These five stories find *Swamp Thing* in a transitional phase. The first three collections in this series walked the line from superheroes to outright terror. But as people began to suspect that *Swamp Thing* might become predictable, Moore gave them a heartwarming, heartbreaking story about cute, immortal aliens hunting their lady; two dream houses and their tragic, magic guardians; a psychedelic love song; and a warning about the perils of the dumping of nuclear waste.

Here, then, are five dreams. Trifles, as the Hystricides puts it, light as air. Or do they, could they, have a darker side? Perhaps that's for you to discover.

Neil Gaiman,
October 1987.

CHAPTER ONE
POG

FROM THE LOG OF THE VIVI-QUINQUEREME "FIND THE LADY":

"CERTAIN ENOUGH, OUR LANDING WAS MORE OR LESS A DISAPPOINTMENT.
"THE TADLING'S PORTAPUDDLE JUST ABOUT DECANTED AGAIN, AND THE JUNIOR UMBRELLA-BIRDS GOT WET HOLDING IT STEADY, OF WHICH THEY ARE FOREVER COMPLAINING.

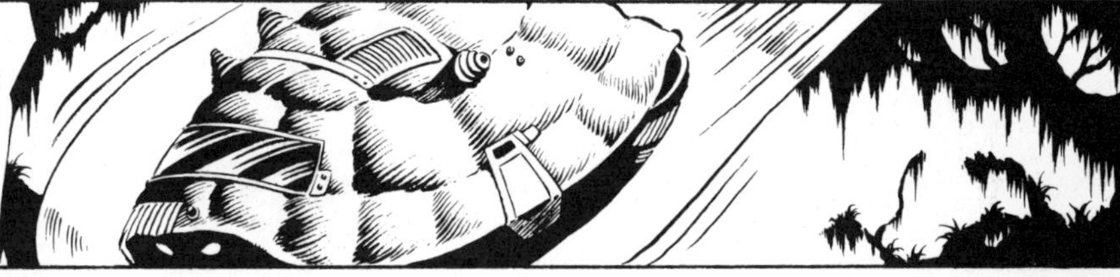
"'FIND THE LADY' HELD UP CONSIDERABLE WELL TO THE ENTRY-BURN, SO IT APPEARS THAT DR. STRIGIFORME WAS WRONG ABOUT THAT... BUT THEN HE MOSTLY IS, THESE WHILES.

"MYSELF AND FRONT-MATE BARTLE FOUND OURSELVES OCCUPIED WRESTLING THE HYSTRICIDE INTO HIS DANGLEWEB, TO STOP HIM ROLLING AROUND PUNCTURING HIS SKIN.
"APLODONTIA USED TO HANDLE HIM SO EASY. I WISH SHE WAS STILL ALIVE.

"HE WAS RAVING FEARSOMELY BAD. JUST BEFORE US MAKING OUR FIRST BOUNCE, I HEARD HIM SHOUT 'THERE IS NO LADY!' AND THEN 'TRIFLES! TRIFLES LIGHT AS AIR!'
G-1602

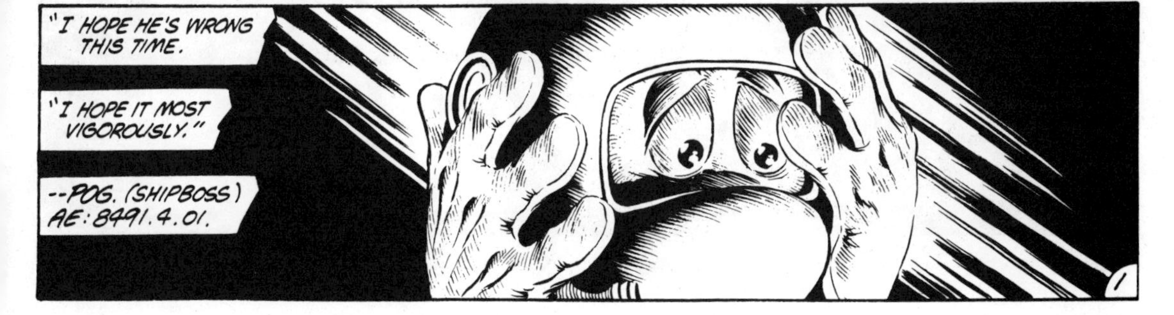
"I HOPE HE'S WRONG THIS TIME.
"I HOPE IT MOST VIGOROUSLY."
--POG. (SHIPBOSS) AE: 8491.4.01.

an ALAN MOORE (WRITER) . SHAWN McMANUS (GUEST ARTIST) . KAREN BERGER (EDITOR) . JOHN COSTANZA (LETTERER) Presentation

FNIF

MHHM.
ATMOSPHERICALS ABOUT TOLERABLE TO MIDDLING, AND GRAVITIES SUFFICIENT TO KEEP THE STUMP-WATER SETTING IN THE STUMP.
BY MY CALCULATEMENTS, YOU CAN DISENTRAIL WITH COMPLETE DIPLOMATIC IMPUNITY...

CHUK

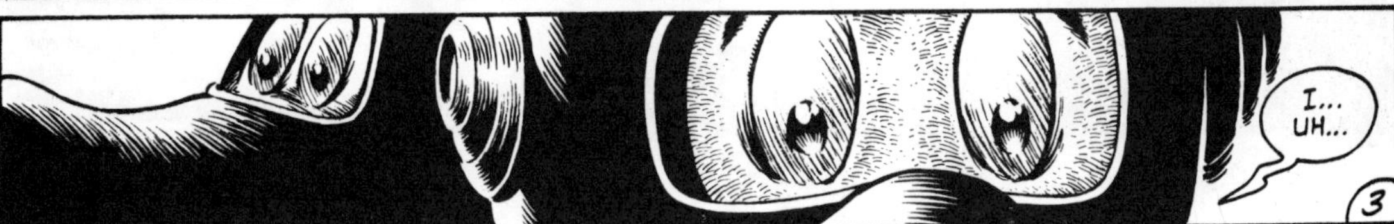
I... UH...

I... THINK WE FOUND THE LADY.

WE FOUND HER? AFTER ALL THESE INTERMINATIONS AND MILLENDERINGS? YOU'RE NOT ABMUSING ME, BOSS?
MAKING ABMUSEMENTS? ABOUT THE LADY? DEFINFINITELY NOT!
GO HELP DISTRANGLE THE HYSTRICIDE AND TELL THE UMBRELLABIRDS TO BREAK OUT THE SKIPS...

...AND DON'T BE UNMEMBERED TO TELL THE TADLING, AND SEE IF OLD STRIGIFORME IS FETCHABLE NOWABOUTS...
A NEW LADY! A NEW LADY AS ENVIRGINOMENTAL AS THE OLD ONE!
HUFF! SOUNDS LIKE AN INCOPROBULL DISLUSION TO ME.

THERE IS NO LADY, SAVE HER LONG SINCE ABANDONED TO THE LONELIEST ANIMALS OF ALL.
WE SEARCH AND ROOTLE 'MIDST THE NEBULAE, MERELY TO OCCUPY OUR TEDIOUS IMMORTALHOOD! WE...
WE...
UH...

HUMF.
I...
I AM OF A SUDDEN BECOME QUITE UNACCOUNTABLY LACHRYMOUS...

IT *LOOKS* LIKE HER. IT SMELLS LIKE HER...
OF COURSE, IT CANNOT ACTUALLY *BE* HER, NOT IN *THIS* REGRETERNAL MISERIVERSE, BUT...
BUT...
PESTIMISTIC OLD SOURQUILL! AS CO-CREATURE AND SHIPBOSS, I COMMASK YOU TO SHUSH YOUR CYANICISMS!
LET'S HOP A SKIP AND SEE IF THERE'S *LOGICAL ANIMALATIONS* HEREBY...
WITH RELIGHTED DELUCTANCE, I FOLLOW.
PSSHH! LUCCA YONDER-WARDS...
UH...
HELLO, CUZLING.
IS THIS *YOUR* LADY WE'RE TREADLING ACROSS?

PERHAPS HE JUST FEELS UN-PARTIAL TO PROVERBALIZING RIGHT NOW...
HMM. IT'S HARD TO CONFIGURE THE ANGLES ON A FAUREIGNA, ESPECIALLY WHEN HE'S INVERTICALLY INCLINED.

OH, THEY'LL COME AROUNDWAYS AND SPLIT THE DIFFERACIAL. THEY JUST LIKE US, ONLY MORESO ANTISOCIABLE AND A MITE SMALLER...
...WHICH IS PECURIOUS, CONSITUATING THAT THEIR LADY IS SO BIG.

BIG ENOUGH FOR US TO REPOPLICATE AND RAISE OUR CELLU-LITTERS?
ENOUGH, AND ENOUGHER STILL!
JUST WISH THE OTHERS HAD SURVAILED LONG ENOUGH TO WATCH THEIR TUBE-TYKES SPROGGING UP...

STILL, LEASTWISE OLD "FIND THE LADY" WON'T OBLIGED TO SING THE EXTINCT-SONG NO MORE, NOW WE'RE HEREABOUTS...
THAT'S A MERCY AND A DELIVERATION. HE WAS STARTING TO UNMEMBER THE WORDS, AND...

WHUURP!
POG?

ARE YOU UNCONTUDED?
FORTUNATURALLY, I AM. I JUST SKITTLED OVER THIS HERE...
OVER THIS...

SWAMP THING
CREATED BY
LEN WEIN and BERNI WRIGHTSON

THAT UNTOLLIGIBLE GRUTTERING... CAN THAT BE A REAL LINGUISH?
WHO CARES? IT'S GOING TO SPLASTER US ALL OVER ITS SWOMPING GROUND!
GOOD BYE-AND-BYE, OLD POG...

EVERYBODY CLUTCH FOR THE CUMULATIONS AND REMAIN EMOTIONLESS!!

PRECARE FOR A DEMONSTRI-FICATION, YOU SHUMBLING SCUMBOGGERY!
NO, STRIGIFORME! THAT SPOTGUN'S A RUSKERY GENTIQUE!

SEE?
WORKS SMOOTH AS A NEW-BOUGHT BABY-BEAKER'S BASE!

FETCH SOME ANIMANACLES, AND STAREFUL AS YOU GO! THERE'S PROSSIBLY MORE OF THESE MUDSTERS LOUCHING HEREAROUND!
YOU UNDISTRAUGHTED YET, BOSS?

I'M... I'M WELL AS CAN BE INSPECTED, BARTLE...
IT'S JUST... WHEN I SAW THAT SHAPERITION, I THOUGHT... I THOUGHT IT WAS...
...THE LONELIEST ANIMAL OF ALL?

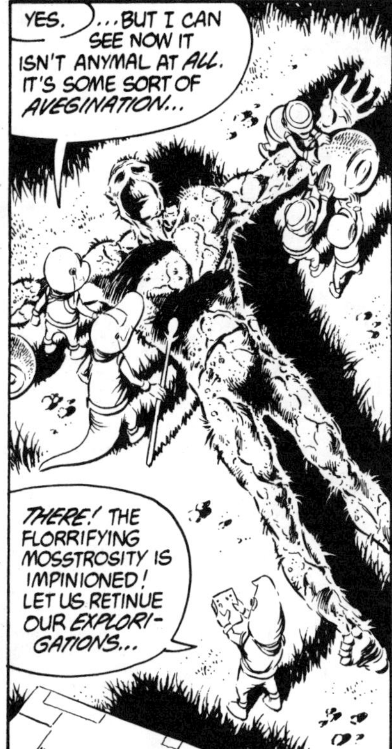
YES.
...BUT I CAN SEE NOW IT ISN'T ANYMAL AT ALL. IT'S SOME SORT OF AVEGINATION...
THERE! THE FLORRIFYING MOSSTROSITY IS IMPINIONED! LET US RETINUE OUR EXPLORI-GATIONS...

OH, YOU TROTTLE ON AFOREWARDS.
I CONTEND TO JUST SET HEREWHILES.
WELL, IF YOU'RE SURE YOU'RE SETTLED IN COMPLETE LUXECURITY, WE'LL GO AND INQUEST AFTER SOME MORE CUZLINGS.

UH...
HELLO?

SEEMS I WAS UNCONFUTABLE IN MY QUESTIMATION. THAT *IS* SOME VARIETY OF LINGUISH YOU'RE DECLAMMERING.
YOU'RE AN INTELLICOMMUNICATING LIFE-FORM!

HMM. I DON'T MUCH CARE TO SEE A CO-CREATURE ENSTRAINED. SAW AN EXCESSANT SUM OF INDIQUITIES LIKE THAT BACK ON THE *OLD* LADY.
I'M GOING TO DISPOWER THE ANIMANACLES.
PLEASE DON'T DISCORPSIFY ME.

L-LIKEWISE.

I KNEW YOU WOULDN'T BE ANTAGRAVATED. YOU'RE MADE OUT OF THE SAME INGREENIENTS AS THE LADY.
YOU MUST BE HER GUARDINER, OR SOME SUCH.

I CONFIGURE WE MUST HAVE STARTLIZED YOU AS MUCH AS REVICE-VERSIONAL. I WISH I COULD EXPLACATE, BUT I DON'T SQUEAK YOUR LINGUISH, SO...
WHAT ARE YOU DROODLING?

SPIKTURES AND ANIMAGLYPHS? YOU THINK WE COULD COMMUNIFY IN PICTOMIME?

WELL, I GUESS THAT'S HOW WE FIRST MANAGED INTER-SPEECHES CONVERGATION BACK ON THE OLD LADY, BUT...
...BUT I'M NOT ENTIRE RESURED I CAN RECONNECT HOW TO DO IT ANYMORE.

"YOU SEE, WE'VE BEEN WANDERLOST FOR SO LONG, AND WE'VE UNMEMBERED SO MUCH..."

...STILL, I'LL TRY AND TURN MY BEST PAW TO IT.
OUR OLD LADY HAD TWO ILLUNAMATIONS, AND A ROCKLETTING ORBITIARA. SHE WAS GLORGEOUS.
YOU CAN'T TELESCRUT-INATE HER FROM HERE-ABOUTS.

ALL OF CRITTERDOM CONFRATERNATED PLEASABLY, AND NOKIND LAUNCHED A PRESUMPTIVE STRIFE AGAINST NO OTHERKIND.
WE SHOWED NO DISREGLECT OF OUR LADY, AND SHE SHOWED NONE TO US.

BUT THERE WAS ONE SOLITRIBAL BREED OF MISANTHROPOMORPHS WHO REFUSED TO CONVIVICATE WITH ELSEFOLK.
THEY CONSTRICTED THEIR OWN UNCIVILIZATION, AND EXCLUCIFIED ANYKIND ELSE FROM JOINING IT.

THEY WERE THE LONELIEST ANIMALS OF ALL.
THEY TOOK OUR LADY AWAY FROM US...
AND THROUGH ALL THE LONG SINCEWHILES WE'VE BEEN QUESTERING FOR A NEW LADY...

"...WITH TRANQUATIC SLAKES DEEP ENOUGH TO DROWSE OUR BEGREAVEMENTS."

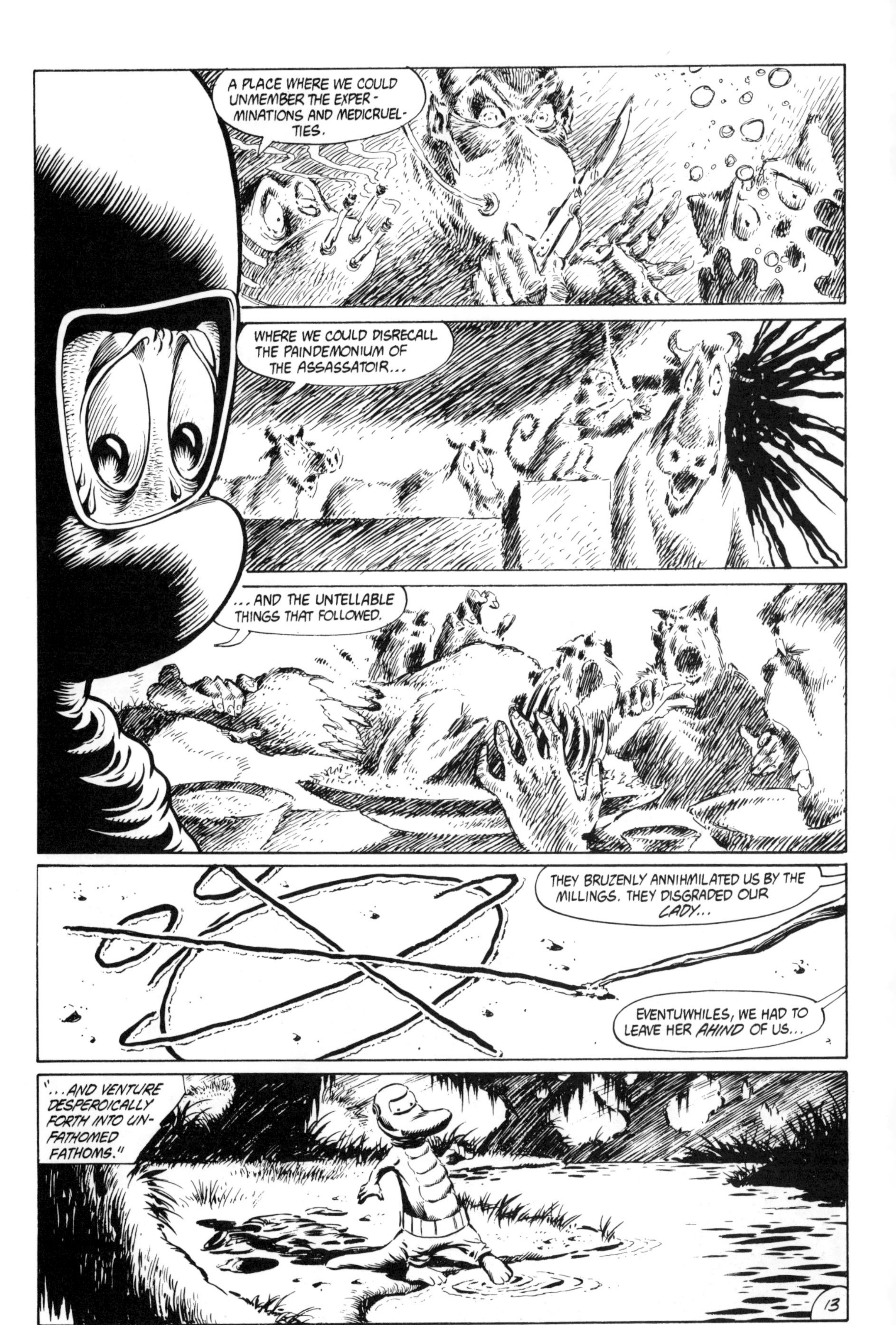
A PLACE WHERE WE COULD UNMEMBER THE EXPER-MINATIONS AND MEDICRUEL-TIES.
WHERE WE COULD DISRECALL THE PAINDEMONIUM OF THE ASSASSATOIR...
...AND THE UNTELLABLE THINGS THAT FOLLOWED.
THEY BRUZENLY ANNIHMILATED US BY THE MILLINGS. THEY DISGRADED OUR LADY...
EVENTUWHILES, WE HAD TO LEAVE HER AHIND OF US...
"...AND VENTURE DESPEROICALLY FORTH INTO UN-FATHOMED FATHOMS."
13

REGRETVIOUSLY, WE COULDN'T ARCOMMODATE EVERYCREATURE...
SO WE SELOTTERIZED *ONE* FROM EACH *SPECIES*.

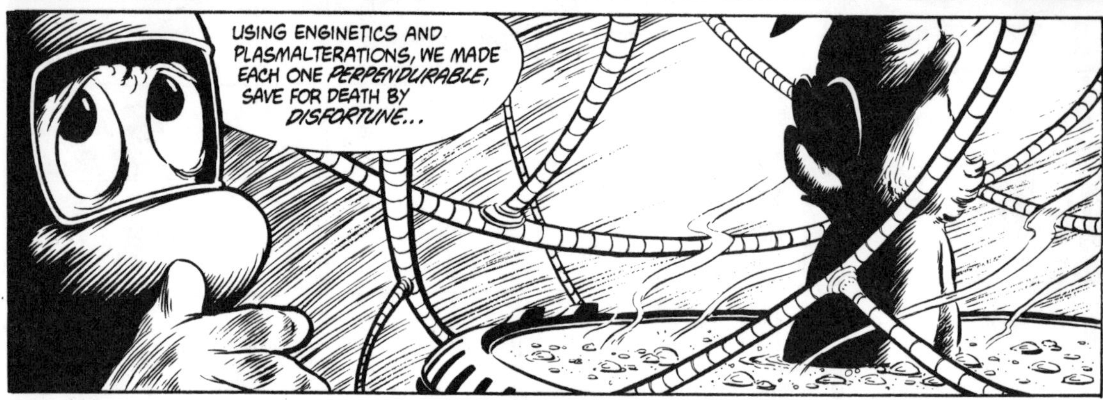
USING ENGINETICS AND PLASMALTERATIONS, WE MADE EACH ONE *PERPENDURABLE*, SAVE FOR DEATH BY *DISFORTUNE*...

AND WE MADE THEM SO THAT CELLULITTERS OF ANYGENDER COULD BE BIRTHED FROM THEIR TISSUE...
... JUST AS SOON AS WE FOUND A NEW LADY WITH ROOM ENOUGH FOR US TO REPROCATE.

THAT WAS IMMEMORILLIONS AGO, AND MOST OF US ARE DEAD LONG SINCETIMES...
...BUT AT LAST WE HAVE ENBEACHED OUR DESPERINATION.

"AT LAST WE CAN REST."

...AND SO THAT'S... HMM?
WHY DID YOU UNSET YOURSELF?
ARE YOU GOING TO DEPASTURE FOR ELSEABOUTS, OR...?

YOU... WANT ME TO ESCOMPANY YOU?
YOU WANT TO DISVEIL SOMETHING TO ME?

WELL, ASSERTAINLY...
...BUT WE MUSTN'T BE UNHASTEFUL, OR MY KINLINGS WILL INFERE THAT YOU'VE UNSCAPED AND DISCORPSIFIED ME.

BATON ROUGE 1 3/4 MILES
RICHIE'S FARM

!

IS IT MUCH DISTANTER?
I'M A TARDLING COMPRIZED WITH YOU, AND NOT SO STRIDEFUL...
OH NO. NOT HERE AS WELL.
THEY CAN'T OWN THIS LADY, TOO!
"WE WERE GOING TO BE HAPPY HERE."
DISPARANT CUZLINGS! LONG-LAST BROODLINGS! LET ME ENGRACE YOU!

"WH-WHY?
"WHY DIDN'T I REACH A REALITIZATION BEFOREWHILES?"
HOW CAN I TELL MY KINLINGS THAT I LET MYSELF BE SEDUPED BY A DISLUSION?
HOW CAN I TELL THE HYSTRICIDE THAT HE WAS RIGHT?
"THAT THERE IS NO LADY..."
...AND THAT IT WAS ALL JUST TRIFLES.
"TRIFLES LIGHT AS AIR."

YYYEEEEEEEE

EEEEEEEEEEEEEEEEEE
BARTLE?
18

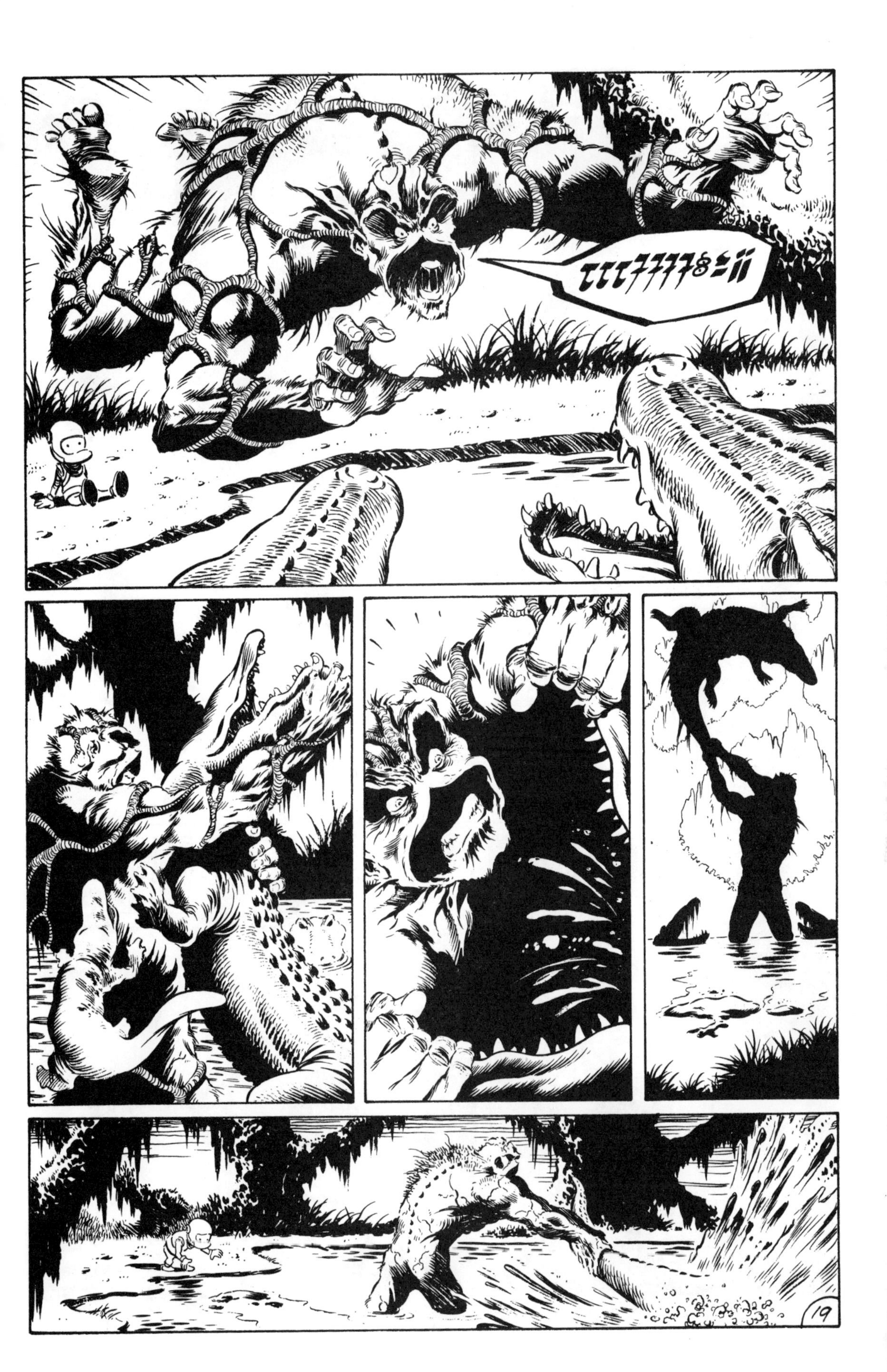

FROM THE LOG OF THE VIVI-QUINQUEREME "FIND THE LADY":
"THIS LADY HAS PREMONSTRATED HER INHOSPATILITY, AND FRONT-MATE BARTLE IS DEAD.
"WE CANNOT REBIDE IN THIS PLACE.

"I COULD SCAREFULLY BARE MYSELF TO TELL THE OTHERS.
"THE HYSTRICIDE, I THINK, WAS THE SOUL MOST ENSTRESSED BY MY DISPOSURE.
"HIS QUILLS BRINDLED, AND HE WOULD NOT LET US TOUCH THE CORPORELIC FOR SOME LITTLE TIME.

"OUR VIVI-QUINQUEREME PERFORMED THE NECROCESSARY EXGRAVATIONS...
"...AND THEN WE DELINQUISHED FRONT-MATE BARTLE TO THE SOIL HE HAD DIED BELIEVING WAS HIS HOME...
"... AND INFINALLY, IT WAS DONE...
"...SAVE FOR THE EXTINCT-SONG.

"'FIND THE LADY' DID HIS BETTERMOST NOT TO UNMEMBER THE WORDS, BUT I FEAR MOST OF THE SACREVERSES ARE LOST TO HIM.
"HE SANG 'DARK, A SOUL WIND BLASTS SO CHILLY...' LUCENTLY ENOUGH, BUT THE REST WAS MUMBLES.
"THE FLORALIEN CREATURE STOOD TO ATTENTIVENESS, ALTHOUGH I DOUBT IT WAS COMPREMOTION-ABLE TO HIM.

"AFTERWHILES, I THANKED HIM FOR HIS SINCERITABLE ATTITUDE.

"THEN WE WENT INBOARD AND ENSHELLTERED OURSELVES...

"...AND 'FIND THE LADY' RESTRACTED HIS CRANIMENTS...

"...AND DISCHARRED HIS ENTREACTORS...

"... AND WE CONTINUED ON OUR WAY."
--POG. (SHIPBOSS) AE: 8491. 4. 01.
NEXT: RITE OF SPRING

CHAPTER TWO
ABANDONED HOUSES

"MRS. CABLE?
"MRS. CABLE... THE APARTMENT IS YOURS, BUT I HAVE TO ASK A COUPLE OF QUESTIONS. IT SAYS HERE THAT YOU'RE MARRIED. WILL MR. CABLE BE LIVING HERE...?
"LIVING HERE...?
"LIVING HERE...?
"I'LL BE HONEST WITH YOU, MRS. CABLE... YOUR HUSBAND IS IN A DEEP COMA, AND THERE IS EVERY INDICATION THAT HE'S LIKELY TO STAY THAT WAY...
"STAY THAT WAY...
"STAY THAT WAY...
"ABBY... WE'RE ALL VERY SATISFIED WITH YOUR WORK HERE AT ELYSIUM LAWNS, BUT I WONDERED IF THINGS WERE OKAY WITH YOU PERSONALLY?
"I WANT TO HELP, ABBY, BUT WITH YOU IT'S ALL SECRETS AND MYSTERIES...
"SECRETS AND MYSTERIES
"SECRETS AND MYSTERIES
"SECRETS AND MYSTERIES"
ABANDONED HOUSE
RON RANDALL ARTIST
ALAN MOORE WRITER
COSTANZA LETTERS
KAREN BERGER EDITOR
1

P-PRETTY SCARY PLACES, AREN'T THEY?
THEY STILL MAKE *ME* NERVOUS... AND I *LIVE* HERE.
WHAT *I* SAY IS, IF YOU CAN'T STAND THE *COLD*, KEEP OUT OF THE *MORTUARY*!

WHO ARE YOU?
AM I DREAMING THIS?
WELL, NOT EXACTLY.. W-WE'RE A PROJECTION OF THE HUMAN UN-CONSCIOUS, EXISTING AS A CONSTRUCT OF THE BRAIN'S RIGHT HEMISPHERE, AND...
IGNORE MY BROTHER. HE HAS NO SENSE OF MYSTERY.
YES. YOU'RE DREAMING THIS.
BUT...BUT...ARE YOU SUPPOSED TO KNOW THAT I'M DREAMING THIS? PEOPLE IN DREAMS DON'T USUALLY...
BANANA OIL! THEY PRETEND NOT TO KNOW TO AVOID EMBARRASSING YOU!
NOW HURRY UP AND CHOOSE!
CHOOSE?
YES... YOUR SUBCONSCIOUS HAS DIRECTED YOU HERE TO LEARN SOMETHING IMPORTANT, YOU SEE, AND...
ARE YOU LOOKING FOR A MYSTERY, OR A SECRET?
I...I DON'T KNOW. IS THERE A DIFFERENCE?
OF COURSE THERE'S A DIFFERENCE! MYSTERIES ARE WONDERS THAT YOU CAN PONDER AND SHARE. SECRETS ARE A BURDEN TO CARRY ALONE!
CHOOSE...
...BETWEEN MY HOUSE OF MYSTERY...
...AND MY BROTHER'S HOUSE OF SECRETS!

WELL...
IF IT'S ALL THE SAME TO YOU, I THINK I'D PREFER A GUIDED TOUR FROM YOUR BROTHER.
NOTHING PERSONAL.
YOUR LOSS, MY DEAR.
I-IS THAT ALL RIGHT? I MEAN, YOU WON'T BE ANGRY, WILL YOU? IF YOU'RE SURE THAT YOU DON'T MIND ME ESCORTING HER...
MIND? WHY SHOULD I MIND?
AM I YOUR KEEPER?
YOUR BROTHER SEEMS PRETTY ABRASIVE. DOESN'T HE GET ON YOUR NERVES?
WELL, HE'S NOT SO BAD. HE JUST GETS JEALOUS WHEN PEOPLE LIKE ME BETTER THAN HIM, I SUPPOSE.
BUT YOU'RE RIGHT...
SOMETIMES HE CAN BE MURDER.
THROUGH HERE.
4

IT'S VERY STRANGE AND CLUTTERED...
YES, YOU'RE RIGHT... THIS IS THE PART OF THE UNCONSCIOUS WHERE ALL THE STORIES ARE BORN AND KEPT.
THERE ARE TOO MANY TO KEEP TIDY, ALTHOUGH GOD KNOWS I TRY...
OVER THERE'S A STORY ABOUT AN OLD WOMAN WHO KEPT THE OCEAN IN A BOTTLE.
DOWN HERE'S THE TALE OF AN ORCHARD THAT BORE SKULLS INSTEAD OF FRUIT. ALL TRUE, YOU KNOW...
THIS WAY...
THERE'S A LOT OF DUST...
HMMM. WELL, THINGS HAVE BEEN QUIET AROUND HERE THESE LAST FEW YEARS. PEOPLE DON'T DROP BY SO MUCH. I THINK THAT'S WHAT ANNOYS MY BROTHER. BEING NEGLECTED...
DOWN HERE...
LISTEN, ARE YOU SURE I'M GOING TO LEARN SOMETHING IMPORTANT FROM ALL THIS...?
OH, YES! MOST CERTAINLY! I'VE GOT A VERY SPECIAL SECRET BACK HERE SOME-PLACE THAT'S JUST FOR YOU!
NOW, WHERE DID I...
AHH!
HERE IT IS!
5

A BRACELET?
BRACELET?
OH, NO! NO, IT JUST LOOKS LIKE A BRACELET. IT'S REALLY A STORY. A SPECIAL CIRCULAR STORY THAT GOES ROUND AND ROUND...
BUT WHAT DOES IT HAVE TO DO WITH ME?
AHHH! NOW, THAT'S THE SECRET!
YOU'RE NOT AN ORDINARY WOMAN, YOU KNOW. SOME STRANGE STORIES HAVE INTRUDED UPON YOUR LIFE LATELY...
STORIES? EVERYTHING THAT'S HAPPENED TO ME HAS BEEN REAL...
OH, PLEASE, IT WAS JUST A FIGURE OF SPEECH. DON'T TAKE OFFENSE. YOU SEE, IN A WAY, EVERYTHING IS MADE OF STORIES.
HERE... DO SIT DOWN...
YOU SEE, WHAT I'M GETTING AT IS, THESE THINGS THAT HAVE HAPPENED TO YOU...
...THEY'VE ALL HAPPENED BEFORE, IN SIMILAR CIRCUMSTANCES!
IT'S LIKE A CIRCLE. IT GOES ROUND AND ROUND AND ROUND...
I'M SORRY, BUT THIS SOUNDS LOONY. I BETTER GO...
OH, NO! PLEASE! YOU MUST LISTEN TO THE STORY...
IT'S ONE OF MY FAVORITES.
IT STARTS LIKE THIS...
"I CANNOT REMEMBER THE MORNING ANYMORE..."

THE EDGE OF THE SWAMP--AND THE MIST-WET OLD MANSION THAT RISES LIKE AN AGING APPARITION INTO A COLD EXPANSE OF SKY--A STATELY SANCTUARY FULL OF BRIGHT LIGHTS AND PROMISES--AND MEMORIES THAT BRING ONLY PAIN...

STORY: LEN WEIN
ART: BERNI WRIGHTSON

I HAVE STOOD WATCHING THAT OLD GRAY EDIFICE FOR MORE LONELY NIGHTS THAN I WANT TO RECALL-- DREAMING ENDLESSLY OF THE SOFT GOLDEN LADY WHO LIVES WITHIN-- KNOWING I CAN NEVER HAVE HER-- WONDERING WHAT SHE'S DOING *NOW*...

YOU SMILE BECAUSE HE EXPECTS YOU TO-- BUT IN THE SHADOWED CORRIDORS OF YOUR HEART THERE IS NO *REAL* JOY-- THERE *NEVER* CAN BE...
A TOAST, MY DARLING-- TO *US!* TODAY IS *SIX MONTHS* SINCE WE WERE *WED!*

YOUR NAME IS *LINDA OLSEN RIDGE*-- AND YOUR MIND IS A RAGING RIVER THIS NIGHT-- CARRYING YOUR THOUGHTS ALONG A SURGING STREAM OF CONSCIOUSNESS-- SENDING *MEMORIES* CRASHING LIKE WAVES UPON SOME DISTANT SHORE...
YOU'RE THINKING ABOUT *ALEX* AGAIN, *AREN'T* YOU, DARLING? I CAN SEE IT IN YOUR *EYES!*
I'M *SORRY,* DAMIAN-- IT'S JUST THAT HE'S STILL SO *REAL* TO ME!
LINDA, ALEX OLSEN IS *DEAD* --AND YOU ARE *MY* WIFE NOW! EVENTUALLY, YOU WILL HAVE TO *REALIZE* THAT FACT! ALEX IS *GONE,* DARLING-- THERE IS *NOTHING* TO DO BUT *FORGET* HIM!

NEVER-- FOR TO FORGET ALEX OLSEN IS TO DENY A PART OF YOURSELF-- A *GOOD* PART-- FILLED WITH HAPPY SUMMER DAYS AND STAR-DAPPLED NIGHTS-- MIST COVERS YOUR EYES-- AND MEMORIES FALL WITH THE TEARS...

WHAT IS A MEMORY? IT IS RIBBONS... CANDLES... A PARTY! YOU HAVE BEEN ALEX'S WIFE FOR TWELVE SHORT MONTHS... IT SEEMS LIKE ONLY YESTERDAY...
HAPPY ANNIVERSARY TO MY TWO DEAREST FRIENDS! I REALLY ENVY YOU, ALEX! YOU GOT YOURSELF QUITE A PRIZE IN LINDA!
AND DON'T THINK I DON'T KNOW IT!
AN ANNIVERSARY GIFT, DARLING-- FOR YOU! A SYMBOL OF MY FEELING FOR YOU!
A GOLDEN BRACELET! LINDA, I...I'LL NEVER TAKE IT OFF AS LONG AS I LIVE! I PROMISE YOU THAT!
WHAT IS A MEMORY? IT IS THE FEELING OF PRIDE YOU HAVE BEING MARRIED TO A FAST-RISING YOUNG SCIENTIST WITH THE WORLD AT HIS DOORSTEP...
WE MAKE A FINE TEAM, DAMIAN-- I DON'T KNOW WHERE I'D BE WITHOUT YOUR HELP!
IF THIS PROJECT SUCCEEDS, ALEX-- THAT WILL BE ALL THE THANKS I NEED!
WHAT IS A MEMORY? IT IS THE SEARING SOUND OF DEVASTATION-- AS YOU WATCH YOUR WORLD GO UP IN FLAMES BEFORE YOU...
OH, DEAR GOD--NO! ALEX'S LAB...
WARAROOOM!
WHAT IS A MEMORY? IT IS THE GAPING WOUND THAT ONCE HAD BEEN YOUR HEART--WHEN YOU LEARN YOU ARE ALONE...
DON'T GO IN THERE! THERE'S NOTHING LEFT TO SEE, LINDA! ALEX IS DEAD!
OH, DAMIAN, NO...NO...NO... NO...NO...

WHAT IS A MEMORY? IT IS A FLEETING FANTASY FAR TOO PAINFUL TO LONG REMAIN--THAT CARRIES YOU BACK THROUGH THE PORTAL OF THE PAST TO THE HARSH REALITY OF NOW...

A HOLLOW RAIN HAS BEGUN TO FALL --AS COLD AND EMPTY AS THE ACHING DEEP WITHIN ME -- I CAN BEAR IT NO LONGER -- THE GRIM, GRAY MANOR STANDS STARK AGAINST THE NIGHT, MOCKING ME -- I BEGIN TO MOVE...

YOU LOOK INTO YOUR HUSBAND'S EYES--AND YOU SEE ONLY SHADOWS--DARK, VEILED THINGS THAT WHISPER TO THE SURFACE--AND QUICKLY FADE AWAY--AND YOU WONDER WHAT IS GOING THROUGH HIS MIND...

"I NEVER REALLY FORGAVE ALEX FOR MARRYING YOU WHEN HE KNEW HOW MUCH I LOVED YOU-- YOU'LL NEVER KNOW HOW HARD IT WAS FOR ME TO KEEP UP THE FACADE OF THE 'ETERNAL FRIEND'..."

"TO SEE YOU EVERY DAY--SO CLOSE AND YET SO IMPOSSIBLY DISTANT--NEVER TO KNOW YOUR TOUCH OR THE FRAGRANCE OF YOUR HAIR--IT WAS MORE THAN I COULD BEAR..."
"IT WAS I WHO ARRANGED THE EXPLOSION--ALONE AT NIGHT IN ALEX'S DARKENED LABORATORY--QUIETLY ALTERING THE VITAL COMPONENTS--TO RID MYSELF OF THE ONLY OBSTACLE IN MY WAY--MY BEST FRIEND..."
"YOU'LL NEVER KNOW THAT ALEX WASN'T KILLED IN THE EXPLOSION--THAT I CARRIED HIS BATTERED AND BLOODY FORM OUT INTO THE FETID INTERIOR OF THE SWAMP BEYOND--AND BURIED IT THERE..."
I WAS EVERY BIT THE BEREAVED FRIEND AT THE FUNERAL--ALWAYS THE COMFORTING SHOULDER--THE TENDER WORD--IT WAS ONLY A MATTER OF TIME UNTIL YOU TURNED TO ME FOR COMFORT--OUR MARRIAGE WAS INEVITABLE!
FORGIVE ME, DARLING--BUT THE CHILL HAS GROWN WORSE! PERHAPS I OUGHT TO RETIRE TO MY ROOM!
OF COURSE, LINDA--HOW THOUGHTLESS OF ME! GO AHEAD... I'LL JOIN YOU SHORTLY!
11

YOU WALK QUIETLY DOWN THE CORRIDOR TO THE SHELTER OF YOUR ROOM-- AND YOU CAN FEEL DAMIAN'S GAZE FOLLOWING YOU-- SEARING TREMORS INTO THE SMALL OF YOUR BACK...
SHE CAN'T BEAR MY TOUCH ANYMORE-- THAT'S THE FIRST SIGN! ALL THE LITTLE SCRAPS OF INFORMATION SHE'S BEEN GATHERING ARE COMING TOGETHER AT LAST!

IT'S ONLY A MATTER OF TIME BEFORE SHE REALIZES THAT I KILLED ALEX--AND THAT WILL MEAN MY END! HOWEVER MUCH I CARE FOR LINDA, MY OWN NECK COMES FIRST... LINDA MUST DIE!

THE CANDLES THAT LIGHT YOUR ROOM PROVIDE THE ONLY REAL WARMTH YOU'VE FELT THIS NIGHT--BUT EVEN THROUGH THAT MELLOW GLOW, THE CHILL RETURNS ONCE MORE...
DAMIAN IS HALF-WAY ACROSS THE HOUSE,.. WHY CAN'T I SHAKE THE FEELING THAT SOMEONE IS WATCHING ME?

MY HEART BEATS SOFTLY ONCE AGAIN--FOR THE SPARKLE IN HER EYES FILLS MY SOUL WITH A JOY I CANNOT DESERVE--LINDA-- HER NAME RINGS LIKE FINE CRYSTAL-- HER HAIR SHINES LIKE GOLD...
LINDA? ARE YOU FEELING BETTER, DARLING?

A LITTLE BETTER, I SUPPOSE, DAMIAN... BUT DON'T WORRY YOURSELF-- IT REALLY IS NOTHING!
NONSENSE! COME-- I'LL MASSAGE YOUR NECK--THAT SHOULD WORK OUT THE CHILL!
I WATCH DAMIAN RIDGE WALK SOFTLY ACROSS THE RUG AND SOMETHING GLITTERS IN HIS HAND-- A HYPODERMIC NEEDLE!

HE STANDS SILENTLY BEHIND HER, THE NEEDLE POISED TO STRIKE -- TO END THE LIFE OF THE ONLY THING IN THIS WORLD THAT MAKES MY EXISTENCE BEARABLE -- THE ONLY REASON I LIVE -- FURY FILLS THE SPACES BEHIND MY EYES -- AND I WALK INTO THE ROOM...

OH, GOD -- *NO!*

CRRASSHHHH!

WITH A SPEED I HAVE NEVER KNOWN BEFORE, I MOVE THE FETID BULK THAT IS MY BODY ACROSS THE SPAN OF FEET -- AND THE CLAW THAT IS MY HAND CLOSES UPON DAMIAN'S WRIST -- CRUSHING IT...

SLOWLY -- CERTAINLY -- I FORCE THE LIFE FROM DAMIAN'S BLACK-HEARTED BODY -- A LIFE HE DOES NOT DESERVE...

FOR SEVERAL SHORT MINUTES, DAMIAN RIDGE STRUGGLES FOR HIS UNWORTHY LIFE -- TEARING, CLAWING, RIPPING DECAYING SHREDS FROM WHAT ONCE HAD BEEN MY FLESH -- UNTIL, AT LAST, HE LIES STILL -- *FOREVER*...

...AND MY BRIGHT, GOLDEN LADY STANDS SCREAMING BEHIND ME...

THE LOATHSOME MONSTROSITY TURNS FROM THE BODY OF YOUR HUSBAND AND REACHES FOR YOU WITH ARMS DRIPPING FILTH--FEAR WELLS UP WITHIN YOU LIKE A FLOOD--AND THE SOUND OF YOUR OWN SCREAMING RINGS IN YOUR EARS...
NO... NO... STAY AWAY... EEEYYYAAAHH!

I STRETCH OUT MY ARMS TO HER--TO CALM HER--TO COMFORT HER--I OPEN MY MOUTH TO TELL HER HOW MUCH I CARE--BUT WHAT ONCE HAD BEEN MY VOCAL CORDS HAVE BEEN SILENT TOO LONG--I CANNOT MAKE A SOUND.

THE TORTURED, SHATTERED LOOK IN HER ONCE-SPARKLING EYES IS MORE THAN I CAN ENDURE--I TURN MY FACE AWAY FROM HER--AND I START TO GO HOME...

ONLY THE SWAMP IS KIND TO ME NOW--IT IS ONLY THE SWAMP THAT CARES--I LOOK DOWN AT MY WRIST--AT THE BARREN PLACE WHERE ONCE THERE WAS A GOLDEN BRACELET--AND I WONDER WHERE IT IS...

--IF TEARS COULD COME--THEY WOULD!

"...AND IF TEARS COULD COME, THEY WOULD."
THE END.
THERE... A SAD LITTLE STORY, ISN'T IT?
BUT... BUT THAT'S ALEC'S STORY!
ALEC HOLLAND... NOT ALEX OLSEN! AND IT DIDN'T HAPPEN AT THE TURN OF THE CENTURY... IT HAPPENED DECADES LATER!
LOOK, WHAT IS THIS?
IT'S THE SECRET! THE SECRET YOU CAME TO LEARN!
ALEC HOLLAND WAS NOT THE FIRST THING TO WALK THE SWAMPS!
THERE WERE OTHERS BEFORE HIM.
BUT... THAT'S IMPOSSIBLE. EVEN ALLOWING FOR COINCIDENCE...
NO! NOT COINCIDENCE! DESIGN!
IN THE HISTORY OF THE WORLD, THERE HAVE COME SOUR TIMES WHEN THE EARTH FEELS COMPELLED TO CREATE AN ELEMENTAL CHAMPION FOR ITSELF.
BUT ALEC'S TRANSFORMATION WAS AN ACCIDENT...
THERE ARE NO ACCIDENTS. SOUR TIMES ARE RETURNING TO YOUR WORLD, AND YOUR WORLD HAS AGAIN SHAPED A PROTECTOR TO STAND AGAINST THEM.
THAT IS WHAT YOU CAME TO LEARN!
NOW FORGIVE ME, BUT IF THE WARNING IS TO BE ANY USE TO YOU, WE MUST HURRY...
HURRY? BUT WHY? I DON'T UNDERSTAND...
15

MY BROTHER! IF I CAN SNEAK YOU OUT BEFORE HE THINKS TO CHECK ON OUR WHERE-ABOUTS, EVERYTHING WILL BE ALL RIGHT...
LOOK, PLEASE, I REALLY CAN'T FOLLOW THIS. IT DOESN'T MAKE SENSE...
IT'S MY FAULT. I'M SO BAD AT EXPLAINING THINGS...
JUST REMEMBER THE STORY OF ALEX OLSEN. TELL YOUR SWAMP THING THE TALE AS I TOLD IT TO YOU...
THEN, WHEN THE TROUBLE STARTS, IT WILL HELP HIM UNDERSTAND HIS PLACE IN THE SCHEME OF THINGS.
IT ISN'T MUCH, BUT IT'S THE BEST I CAN DO.
THROUGH HERE...
MY BROTHER'S PROBABLY BUSY FEEDING HIS GAR-GOYLES RIGHT NOW...
IF YOU GO ACROSS THE GROUNDS AND OUT THROUGH THE GATE, YOU'LL MAKE IT BACK TO WAKEFULNESS WITH THE SECRET INTACT AND READY TO PASS ON...
...BUT THEN IT WOULDN'T BE A SECRET, WOULD IT?
YOU KNOW THE RULES, BROTHER...
...AND NOW YOU MUST PAY THE FORFEIT.

BUT... SHE MUST BE ALLOWED TO TAKE THE STORY WITH HER WHEN SHE LEAVES. HER WORLD IS IN DANGER...
IF SHE WANTED SOMETHING SHE COULD SHARE WITH OTHERS, SHE SHOULD HAVE CHOSEN A MYSTERY...
...FOR SECRETS MUST BE KEPT FOREVER. I WARNED HER...
I... I WON'T LET YOU DO THIS! IT'S JUST BECAUSE YOU'RE JEALOUS...
YOU'VE ALWAYS BEEN JEALOUS!
JEALOUS? OF YOU?
NO... I AM SIMPLY DISGUSTED. WE HAVE BEEN CHARGED, YOU AND I, WITH THE SAFEKEEPING OF THE STORIES. WHO BETTER? WE WERE IN THE FIRST STORY...
NOW YOU WOULD BETRAY THAT TRUST.
WHEN THE WOMAN LEAVES HERE SHE WILL FORGET YOUR LITTLE YARN. IT WILL REMAIN SAFE IN SOME BACKWATER OF HER MIND, IGNORED AS A SECRET SHOULD BE...
NO! I WON'T LET YOU!
UPH
GET OFF OF ME, YOU OBESE SLUG...
I'M WARNING YOU...
GET OFF BEFORE I...

CAIN! NO!
NOT AGAIN!
RUNCH
RUNCH
RUNCH
YOU... YOU MURDERED HIM.
YOUR OWN BROTHER...
MURDER? DON'T TALK TO ME ABOUT MURDER!
I INVENTED MURDER!
18

AS FOR THAT FAT OAF, DON'T WORRY ABOUT HIM. HE'LL BE UP AND ABOUT TOMORROW, BUMBLING AROUND JUST AS GOOD AS NEW...
...AT LEAST UNTIL THE NEXT TIME.
IT'S ALL WE HAVE TO DO NOW THAT NOBODY WANTS TO HEAR THE STORIES ANYMORE.
THE SAME ACT OVER AND OVER AGAIN...
IT'S OUR PUNISHMENT, FOR DOING IT THE FIRST TIME.
BUT WHY SHOULD YOU BOTH BE PUNISHED FOR SOMETHING THAT YOU DID? IT ISN'T FAIR!
OF COURSE IT'S FAIR! I'M BEING PUNISHED FOR BEING THE FIRST PREDATOR...
...AND HE'S BEING PUNISHED FOR BEING THE FIRST VICTIM.
NOW... I THINK IT'S TIME FOR YOU TO LEAVE.
REMEMBER TO TAKE YOUR SECRET WITH YOU. TOO BAD THAT YOU WON'T BE ABLE TO SHARE IT WITH ANYBODY.
WAIT! DON'T LEAVE ME HERE!
HOW CAN I SEE WHERE I'M GOING IN THIS FOG?
HOW AM I SUPPOSED TO FIND MY WAY...
...HOME?
19

WRITE IT DOWN...
WRITE IT DOWN RIGHT AWAY...
HOW DID IT START...?
"I CANNOT REMEMBER THE MORNING ANY..."
BRRING
BRRING
HELLO...? OH...HI, DEANNA. AM I SUPPOSED TO BE AT WORK? ISN'T TODAY SATURDAY?
OH. WELL, I DON'T MIND COMING IF YOU'RE BUSY. NO, THAT'S NO PROBLEM.
SEE YOU IN ABOUT AN HOUR. SURE.
'BYE.
I cannot remember the morning any
"I CANNOT REMEMBER THE..."?
WHAT DID I WRITE THAT FOR?
OH, WELL, THAT'S LIFE...
...FULL OF LITTLE MYSTERIES.
NEXT: RITE OF SPRING

CHAPTER THREE
RITE OF SPRING

SPRING CAME, AND EVERYTHING IN THE WORLD WOKE UP...
G-1693
TERREBONNE PARISH GENERAL HOSPITAL
...EXCEPT HIM.
CAUTION
OXYGEN TENT IN USE
OUTSIDE, THE RUDE YOUNG TENDRILS, SUPPLE AND GREEN, MUSCLED UPWARD THROUGH CHINKS IN THE TURF'S DARK UNDERBELLY.
THE DOCTOR SAID THERE WAS LITTLE INDICATION OF HIGHER BRAIN ACTIVITY. HE WAS NOT EXPECTED TO RECOVER.
YES, SHE FELT GUILTY, FELT RELIEVED, FRIGHTENED, ANGRY, ALL THOSE THINGS...
...BUT THE SEPARATE SHADES OF HER GRIEF HAD MERGED, LIKE VIVID MODELING-CLAYS CRUSHED TOGETHER, INTO A SINGLE MAUVE-BROWN BRUISE.
BRUISES FADE EVENTUALLY.
THE DOCTOR VENTURED THAT SUCH A BEAUTIFUL YOUNG WOMAN, HER LIFE AHEAD OF HER, WOULD SOON FIND SOMEONE ELSE.
OUTSIDE, BEES JERKED THROUGH THE GLASSY AFTERNOON, THEIR HIND LEGS DIPPED IN POWDERED GOLD.
RUIZ
THEY'D SPRAYED THE PLANTS IN THE LOBBY. DIAMONDS OF PERSPIRATION GLISTENED ON SKINS OF COOL AND BURNISHED GREEN.
SHE FELT AN ACHE, BUT NOT OF MOURNING.
SHE KNEW WHO SHE WANTED TO BE WITH.

CREATED BY LEN WEIN
SWAMP THING
AND BERNI WRIGHTSON
RITE of SPRING
ALAN MOORE
WRITER
STEPHEN BISSETTE & JOHN TOTLEBEN
ARTISTS
KAREN BERGER
EDITOR
JOHN COSTANZA
LETTERER

DO YOU MIND IF I...?
NO.
PLEASE... TAKE IT...

Y'KNOW... THE WAY YOU LOOK...
I THINK I LIKE YOU *BEST* IN SPRING.

OH YES.

YES, VERY MUCH,

THEN... YOU MUST NOT... TORTURE YOURSELF... WITH POINTLESS GUILT...
IF... THERE IS... SOMEONE... THAT YOU LOVE... THEN TELL THEM...
YEAH, WELL...
THAT'S, Y'KNOW...
THAT'S WHAT I'M TRYING TO DO.
YOU MEAN...
...ME...?
OH, FOR GOD'S SAKE...
WHO ELSE?
5

OH NO.
I'VE RUINED IT, HAVEN'T I? I'VE SCREWED IT UP...
I SHOULD NEVER HAVE SAID...

LOOK...LET'S JUST FORGET IT. I'LL GO HOME NOW, AND WE'LL FORGET I SAID ANYTHING.
I MEAN, IT'S JUST SO RIDICULOUS, RIGHT? IT'S IMPOSSIBLE, IT'S BIZARRE, IT PROBABLY ISN'T EVEN LEGAL...

OH HELL.
THERE'S SOMETHING WRONG WITH ME. I BUILD THINGS UP IN MY MIND...
I READ THINGS INTO THE WAY YOU LOOK AT ME, KID MYSELF THAT MAYBE YOU FEEL THE SAME AS I DO, BUT...

YOU'RE A PLANT, FOR GOD'S SAKE!
JUST SAYING IT OUT LOUD, I MEAN, IT'S JUST SO FUNNY!
HOW COULD YOU LOVE ME?

6

DEEPLY...
SILENTLY...
...AND...FOR TOO MANY... YEARS.

YOU...
YOU NEVER SAID.

NO. I THOUGHT... IT WOULD... *FRIGHTEN* YOU...
ABBY...?
WHAT...DO WE DO...NOW?

I'VE... NEVER KISSED YOU...
IT...WOULD BE...*UNPLEASANT* FOR YOU, ABBY...WE ARE SO...*DIFFERENT*...

OH.
IT'S LIKE LIME, BUT...
...BUT NOT AS *SHARP*.

CONTINUED ON 2ND PAGE FOLLOWING.

TOTLEBEN
83/84

WELL, LISTEN...
I MEAN, I HAVE, Y'KNOW, *THOUGHT* ABOUT ALL THAT, BUT...
I MEAN, I *KNOW* THAT... THE PHYSICAL SIDE OF THINGS... I KNOW THAT'S NOT POSSIBLE, BUT...

LOOK, WHAT I'M *SAYING* IS THAT IT'S NOT IMPORTANT. NOT TO ME.
AS LONG AS ALL THE *OTHER* STUFF IS THERE. AS LONG AS YOU... WELL, *WANT* ME, I GUESS, AND SORT OF CARE ABOUT ME...

BUT THERE... SHOULD BE... *SOME* FORM... OF COMMUNION...

9

POK

YEAH. YEAH, I KNOW, BUT...
...BUT IT DOESN'T HAVE TO BE *PHYSICAL*.

NO.
PLEASE...
WAIT HERE... FOR A MOMENT...

UH...
WHAT YOU WANT ME TO, UH...
WHAT, YOU MEAN, LIKE, I'M SUPPOSED TO, UH...
...EAT IT?
10

YES.
DOES... THE IDEA... REPEL YOU...?
N-NO, NOT ANY-MORE...
THE FIRST TIME... THE FIRST TIME I THOUGHT ABOUT SOMEBODY EATING PART OF YOU, I...
WELL, I THREW UP.
BUT... IF THIS IS LIKE, SOMETHING THAT YOU WANT ME TO DO...
GMNMM...
THIS IS REALLY GOOD.
YOU WANTED TO DO THIS AS, LIKE, A SYMBOLIC THING?
NO...
NOT... ENTIRELY...

IT IS...
WELL, OKAY.
UH...
RIGHT. HERE GOES...
...NMUF...
S'GREAT...
S'LIKE A SORT OF PERFUME TASTE... LIKE CARDAMOM...
WHAT DO YOU MEAN?
IS THERE SOMETHING ELSE I SHOULD HAVE...
UH...
ALEC...?
ALEC... EVERYTHING LOOKS SORT OF...
...STRANGE...
HOW... DO YOU MEAN... "STRANGE"...?
ALEC?
ALEC... I...
OH.
OHHH...

OH, LOOK AT THE SWAMP...
IT'S ALL OF FIRE... MILLIONS OF BIRTHDAY CANDLES...
AND... LOOK AT ME! ALL THESE STRANDS OF PEARLY STUFF...
ALEC... WHAT'S HAPPENED TO EVERYTHING?
YOU ATE... THE FRUIT... ABBY...
YOU ABSORBED... A LITTLE... OF MY CONSCIOUSNESS...
...MY PERCEPTIONS...
YOU MEAN...
YOU MEAN... THIS... IS HOW YOU SEE THINGS?
NOT... ALL... OF THE TIME...
ONLY... WHEN I... WISH TO.
DO YOU... LIKE IT?

OH, IT'S...
THESE *STRANDS*... *YOU'RE* MADE OF THEM, TOO...
EVERYTHING'S MADE OF THEM... SILKY, LUMINOUS COBWEBS...
AND THESE LITTLE STARS... THESE LITTLE JEWELS OF LIGHT THAT DRIFT ABOUT *INSIDE* YOU...
I DON'T HAVE ANY OF *THOSE*...
NO. THOSE... ARE *INSECTS*...
EVERYTHING'S *ALIVE* AND...
... AND IT'S ALL MADE FROM THE *SAME STUFF!*
I NEVER *REALIZED*...
I NEVER REALIZED...
... THAT THE WORLD...
... WAS LIKE *THIS*...

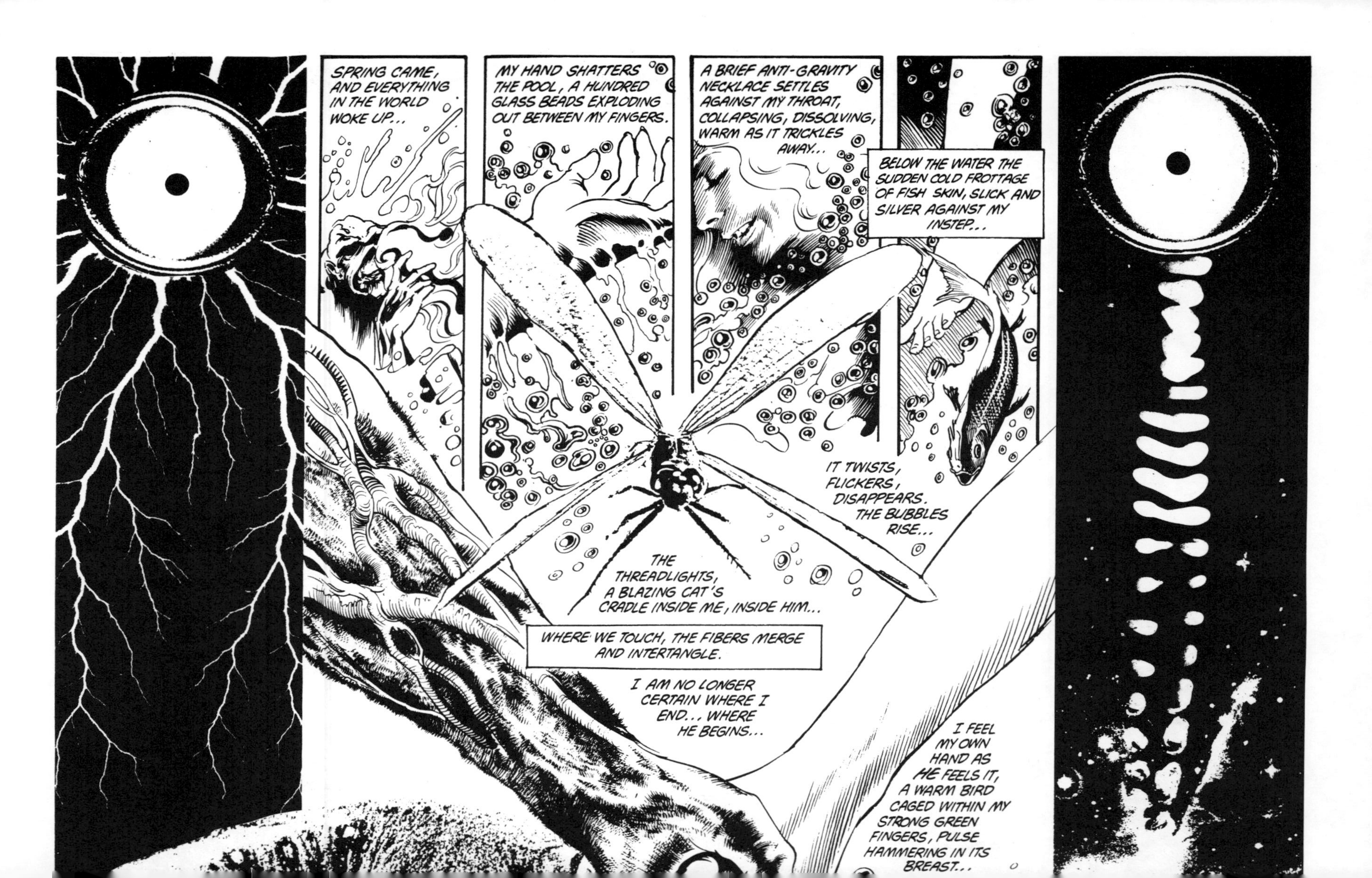
SPRING CAME, AND EVERYTHING IN THE WORLD WOKE UP...
MY HAND SHATTERS THE POOL, A HUNDRED GLASS BEADS EXPLODING OUT BETWEEN MY FINGERS.
A BRIEF ANTI-GRAVITY NECKLACE SETTLES AGAINST MY THROAT, COLLAPSING, DISSOLVING, WARM AS IT TRICKLES AWAY...
BELOW THE WATER THE SUDDEN COLD FROTTAGE OF FISH SKIN, SLICK AND SILVER AGAINST MY INSTEP...
IT TWISTS, FLICKERS, DISAPPEARS. THE BUBBLES RISE...
THE THREADLIGHTS, A BLAZING CAT'S CRADLE INSIDE ME, INSIDE HIM...
WHERE WE TOUCH, THE FIBERS MERGE AND INTERTANGLE.
I AM NO LONGER CERTAIN WHERE I END... WHERE HE BEGINS...
I FEEL MY OWN HAND AS HE FEELS IT, A WARM BIRD CAGED WITHIN MY STRONG GREEN FINGERS, PULSE HAMMERING IN ITS BREAST...

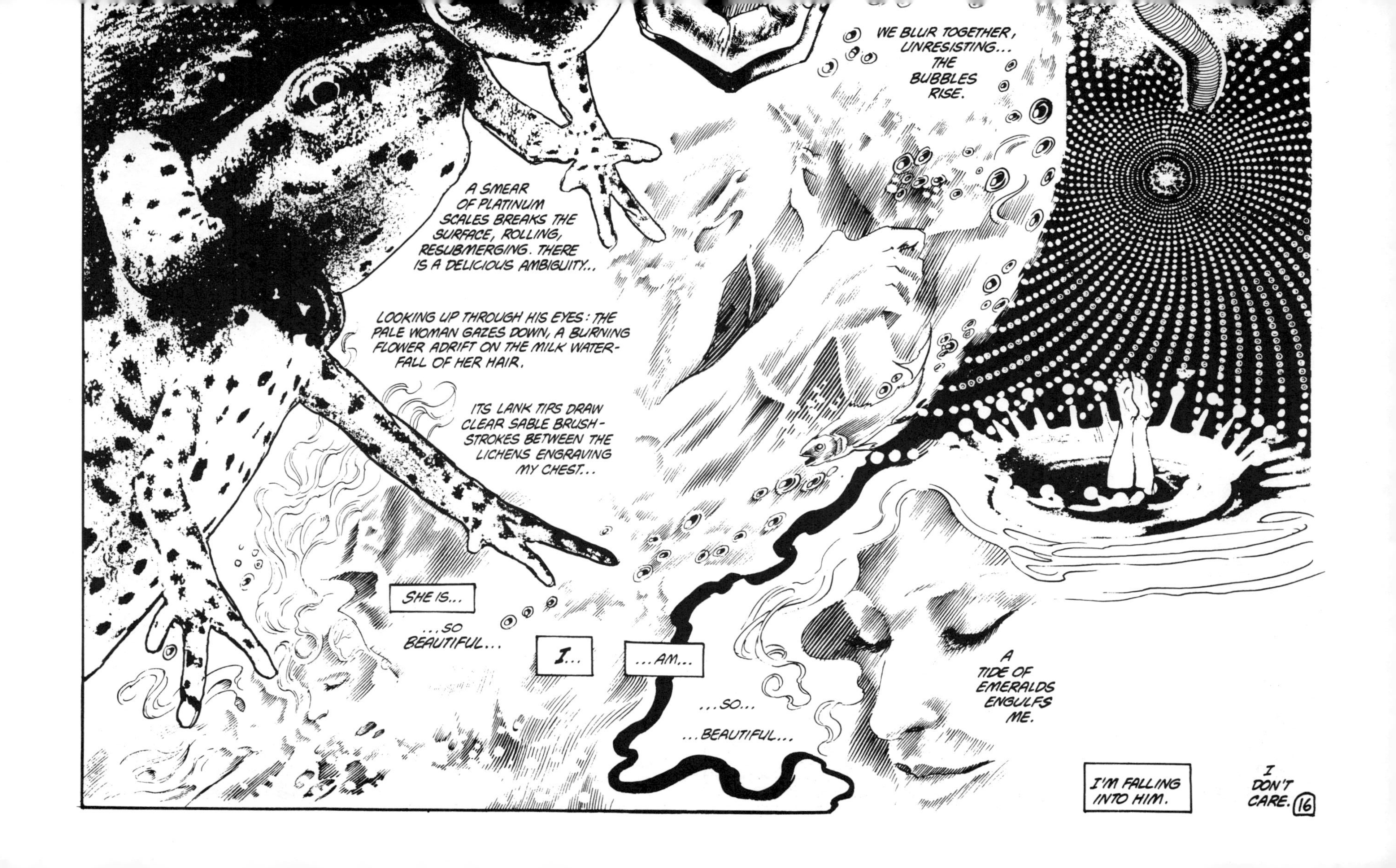
A SMEAR OF PLATINUM SCALES BREAKS THE SURFACE, ROLLING, RESUBMERGING. THERE IS A DELICIOUS AMBIGUITY...
LOOKING UP THROUGH HIS EYES: THE PALE WOMAN GAZES DOWN, A BURNING FLOWER ADRIFT ON THE MILK WATER-FALL OF HER HAIR.
ITS LANK TIPS DRAW CLEAR SABLE BRUSH-STROKES BETWEEN THE LICHENS ENGRAVING MY CHEST...
WE BLUR TOGETHER, UNRESISTING... THE BUBBLES RISE.
SHE IS...
...SO BEAUTIFUL...
I...
...AM...
...SO...
...BEAUTIFUL...
A TIDE OF EMERALDS ENGULFS ME.
I'M FALLING INTO HIM.
I DON'T CARE.
16

IN HIM, I RIDE THE AMBER SAP, OOZING THROUGH MINIATURE LABYRINTHS. CLUSTERS OF INSECT EGGS BURN LIKE NEBULAE, SUSPENDED IN THEIR UNIQUE AND VINE-WROUGHT COSMOS...
THROUGH HIM, I SPRAWL WITH THE SWAMP, SOPPING, STEAMING, DRAGONFLIES STITCHING NEON THREADS THROUGH THE DAMP AIR SURROUNDING ME...
BEYOND HIM I WRESTLE THE PLANET, SUNK IN LOAM TO MY ELBOWS AS IT ARCHES BENEATH ME, TUMBLING ENDLESSLY THROUGH ENDLESS INK.
THE BARK ENCRUSTS MY FLANKS. THE MOSS CLIMBS MY SPINE TO EMBRACE MY SHOULDERS...
WE... ARE... ONE CREATURE...
...AND ALL...
...THAT THERE IS...
...IS IN US...

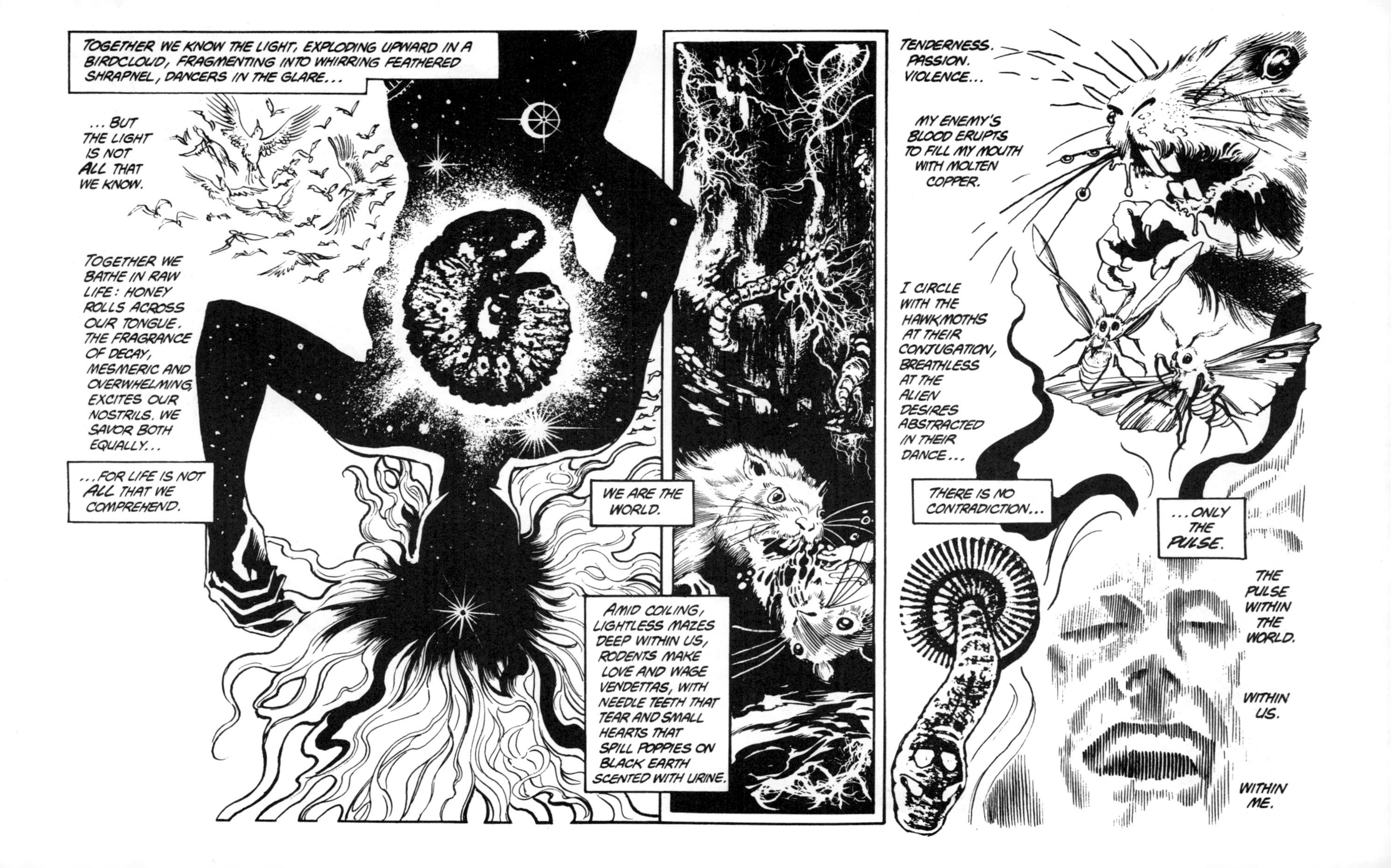
TOGETHER WE KNOW THE LIGHT, EXPLODING UPWARD IN A BIRDCLOUD, FRAGMENTING INTO WHIRRING FEATHERED SHRAPNEL, DANCERS IN THE GLARE...
...BUT THE LIGHT IS NOT ALL THAT WE KNOW.
TOGETHER WE BATHE IN RAW LIFE: HONEY ROLLS ACROSS OUR TONGUE. THE FRAGRANCE OF DECAY, MESMERIC AND OVERWHELMING, EXCITES OUR NOSTRILS. WE SAVOR BOTH EQUALLY...
...FOR LIFE IS NOT ALL THAT WE COMPREHEND.
WE ARE THE WORLD.
AMID COILING, LIGHTLESS MAZES DEEP WITHIN US, RODENTS MAKE LOVE AND WAGE VENDETTAS, WITH NEEDLE TEETH THAT TEAR AND SMALL HEARTS THAT SPILL POPPIES ON BLACK EARTH SCENTED WITH URINE.
TENDERNESS. PASSION. VIOLENCE...
MY ENEMY'S BLOOD ERUPTS TO FILL MY MOUTH WITH MOLTEN COPPER.
I CIRCLE WITH THE HAWKMOTHS AT THEIR CONJUGATION, BREATHLESS AT THE ALIEN DESIRES ABSTRACTED IN THEIR DANCE...
THERE IS NO CONTRADICTION...
...ONLY THE PULSE.
THE PULSE WITHIN THE WORLD.
WITHIN US.
WITHIN ME.

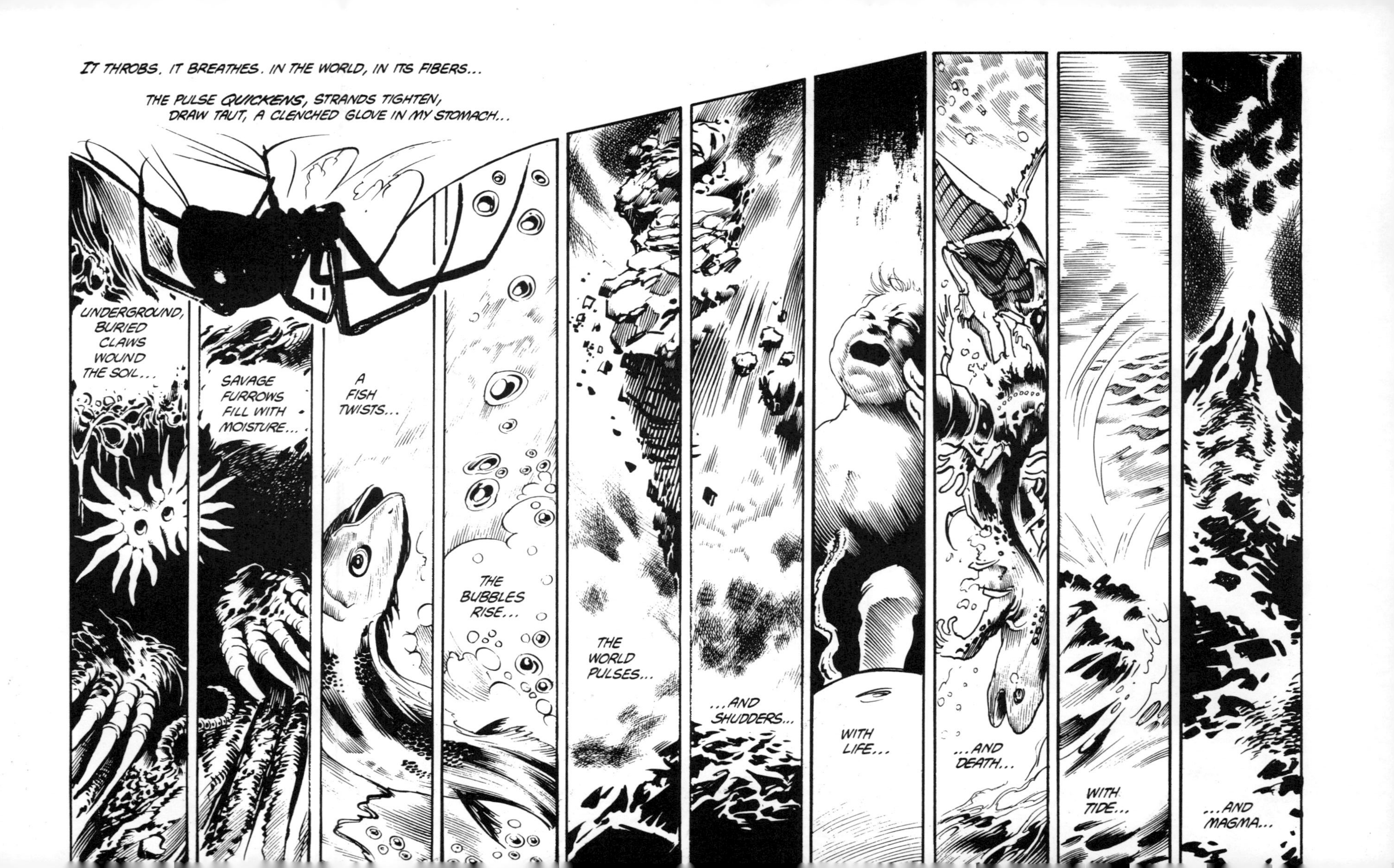
IT THROBS. IT BREATHES. IN THE WORLD, IN ITS FIBERS...
THE PULSE QUICKENS, STRANDS TIGHTEN, DRAW TAUT, A CLENCHED GLOVE IN MY STOMACH...
UNDERGROUND, BURIED CLAWS WOUND THE SOIL...
SAVAGE FURROWS FILL WITH MOISTURE...
A FISH TWISTS...
THE BUBBLES RISE...
THE WORLD PULSES...
...AND SHUDDERS...
WITH LIFE...
...AND DEATH...
WITH TIDE...
...AND MAGMA...

WITH ME.
WITH HIM.
....

DOES THIS... UH...
DOES THIS MEAN WE'RE GOING OUT?

nExt: "THE NUKEFACE PAPERS I"

CHAPTER FOUR
THE NUKEFACE PAPERS

Part One

PROLOGUE:
While his lover sleeps, the swamp creature sits in the smoldering pink dusk and overlooks his territories.
To the east, paperboys have wearied halfway through their rounds, dumping their remaining papers somewhere discreet and telling the newsagent he must have miscounted. The dead headlines dance upon a lukewarm wind, monochrome tumbleweed bowling through the failing light.
He watches the sheets of newsprint flap like huge moths, crippled by their own weight, hopping clumsily amongst the black trees. Their pages are full of obsolete tragedies and discarded faces; all the carefully logged hysteria of a world he no longer belongs to.
Behind him, his lover mumbles three dream-submerged syllables, but does not wake, and he is content beneath a darkening and volcanic sky. The swamp engulfs them. It is their own damp cosmos, and the troubles of the world beyond seem no more than the whispered conversations of distant madmen...

ED?

ED? I WANNA ~ULP~ TELLYA SOMETHIN'...

I'M AN AMERICAN, ED. Y'KNOW WHAT I MEAN BY THAT?
I MEAN... I AM A CITIZEN OF AMERICA.
THAT'S THE UNITED STATES OF AMERICA, ED...

MY NAME AIN'T ED.
Y'KNOW... I'M COLD.

THAT'S BECAUSE IT'S NIGHTTIME, ED. I'LL LIGHT A FIRE...
WHY DON'TYA LIGHT A FIRE?
THAT'S WHAT I SAID! DAMMIT, ED, I JUST SAID I WAS GONNA LIGHT A FIRE...

SOME PAPER...
GOTTA MATCH HERE SOMEPLACE...
~UP~
Radioactive Pedestals
Nuclear Accident

THERE...
SKKRIIIT!

"The NUKE-FACE papers part 1"
SWAMP THING
CREATED BY LEN WEIN and BERNI WRIGHTSON
* Alan Moore: WRITER
* Stephen Bissette and
John Totleben: ARTISTS
* Karen Berger: EDITOR
* Tatjana Wood: colorist
* John Costanza: letterer
THERE'S GLORY FOR YA...
By Toxic Fumes, Are Dead on L.I.
Vere Cleaning Cesspool _3d Worker Injured
By JOSEPH BERGER
ment worried
Vashed-up waste
T.V.A. Lays Off
Over Nuclear Pl
Special to The New York Times
3

IT'S BOB.
MY NAME'S BOB.
GULP

"BOB"... "ED"... THESE DAYS, WHO CARES?
NOBODY GIVES A DAMN ANYMORE, AN' THAT'S THE HONEST TRUTH...

MRS. MEREL THREW ME OUTTA THE HOUSE. SHE WENT CRAZY AND STABBED ME INNA HIP WITH A NAIL FILE.
THAT'S WHY I'M OUT HERE...
SNIT

WELL, MYSELF, ED, I'M A PENNSYLVANIA MAN...
GLEN MILLER WROTE A SONG ABOUT PENNSYLVANIA ONCE...
OUTTA JUICE.
PLUP!

DADADALADADA DA DA
HERE... Y'WANNA TRY SOME O' MINE?

DADADALADADA DA DA...
...AN' THEN THEY ALL SHOUT "PENNSYLVANIA SIX FIVE THOUSAND!"
GA-LOK
HA HA HA. I REMEMBER...

I REMEMBER THEY PLAYED IT ON PROM NIGHT, AN' I DANCED WITH SISSY AUTREY. HA HA HA...
GGKUHH!
IIIHGKUUH!!
ED?
NYEUGH! PFFUH...
HEH. HITS THE OL' SPOT, DON' IT?
CLLUH... WHAT IS IT? I CAN STILL TASTE IT...
OH, JEEZ, I THINK I SWALLOWED SOME...
GIVE IT A CHANCE. IT GROWS ON YA. YOU JUST SIT BACK AN' LEMME TELLYA 'BOUT PENNSYLVANIA...
SAY, ED...
...HOW 'BOUT HAIR O' THE DOG?
NO?
AAAH, IT DON'T MATTER.
WHAT WAS I TALKIN' ABOUT...?
PLUP!

"OH, YEAH...
"PENNSYLVANIA...
"BLOSSOMVILLE, PENNSYLVANIA. YA HADDA SEE IT BACK INNA SIXTIES, WHEN THERE WAS WORK.
"THEY HADDA BIG EXPLOSION UP AT THE LOMBARD MINE IN '68...
"WHOLE DAMN COAL SEAM CAUGHT FIRE!
"IT'S BIN BURNIN' LIKE THAT FOR SIXTEEN YEAR, NOW...
"NOBODY WORTH SPEAKIN' OF LIVES THERE THESE DAYS.
"JUST MACHINES, Y'KNOW? DEAD OL' MACHINES...
"I WAS THERE TILL A MONTH OR SO BACK, BUT, Y'KNOW, IT ALL WENT T'HELL AN' I HADDA LEAVE..
"TELLYA FER NUTHIN', ED, I WISH I WAS BACK THERE.
6

"I WONDER WHAT THE PEOPLE 'RE DOIN' IN BLOSSOMVILLE TONIGHT?"
WALLACE?
I THOUGHT YOU WERE GOING TO WAIT IN THE CAR, TREASURE.
IT'S COLD...
OH, I GOT BORED.
ARE YOU STILL THINKING ABOUT ALL THAT AWFUL TROUBLE?
IT WASN'T YOUR FAULT.
NO, I REALIZE THAT. IT'S JUST...
OH, I DON'T KNOW. I'M JUST GLAD THAT THE DUMP HERE HAS FINALLY BEEN CLOSED DOWN AND SEALED OFF.
I'M JUST GLAD TO SEE THE BACK OF HIS HELLHOLE.
WALLACE, YOU KNOW, I WISH YOU WOULDN'T USE THAT WORD.
NO. I KNOW. I'M SORRY.
I WAS JUST THINKING...
THIS MUST ALL HAVE SEEMED LIKE SUCH A GOOD IDEA WHEN THEY STARTED OUT.

THE STRIPMINES WERE ALL USED UP AND EMPTY, AND NOBODY BUT THE BUMS AND WINOS EVER CAME NEAR. IT WAS AN IDEAL PLACE TO DUMP THE, Y'KNOW, THE...
THE STUFF.
THE STUFF. YEAH.
THE COMPANY WAS STICKING IT IN THE SLAG PITS UNDER THE OLD LOMBARD MINE. IT WAS SAFE DOWN THERE! THEY DID TESTS!
WALLACE, I KNOW YOU! YOU WOULDN'T BE INVOLVED IF IT WAS SOMETHING THAT COULD HURT PEOPLE.
NO. NO, OF COURSE I WOULDN'T.
BUT THEN THOSE TRAMPS, THOSE BUMS... THEY ALL STARTED VANISHING...
WALLACE, YOU KNOW HOW DERELICTS ARE. THOSE POOR MEN, THEY GET LOST, THEY LEAVE THE AREA...
IT'S GOD'S WILL. YOU CAN'T BLAME YOURSELF.
SAY, DID I TELL YOU ABOUT THAT THING I HEARD THOSE KIDS SAY? ABOUT ONE OF THOSE OLD MEN THAT VANISHED?
THEY SAID HE WAS "OUT ON A BENDER WITH NUKEFACE"
WHAT DOES THAT MEAN, DO YOU THINK?
I DON'T KNOW.
C'MON... IT'S GETTING COLDER. LET'S GET BACK IN THE CAR.
THE COMPANY WANTS US IN LOUISIANA BY NOON TOMORROW...
Nuclear Panel Votes For Proposal to Start 3 Mile Island Plant
By JANE PERLEZ
Special to The New York Times
"O'COURSE, EVERYBODY LEFT BLOSSOMVILLE IN THE END..."

EVEN ME, ED.
I STAYED ON AS LONG AS I COULD AFTER THE '68 BURN-UP...
OWED IT TO OLD JEFF LOMBARD. HE HIRED ME WHEN I WAS FIFTEEN. THE PNEUMONIA TOOK HIM IN '64...
WE ARE NO COWS

I USED TO LIVE OUT IN THE MINE, JUST, Y'KNOW, LOOKIN' AFTER STUFF, KEEPIN' STUFF TIDY...
NUH...
PLUP!

ROUND '72 OR SO, A LOTTA COMPANY PEOPLE CAME ROUND, STARTED PUTTIN' STUFF DOWN IN THE OVERFLOW PITS...
UAH...
AA...

HELL, I DIDN'T KNOW WHAT IT WAS...
BUT, Y'KNOW, WHEN A GUY'S THIRSTY, HE...
ED?
TWEEH

ED? YOU ALL RIGHT?
GETTIN' CHILLY AGAIN, HUH?
MY TOOTH...
MY TOOTH JUST CAME OUT.

WELL, I'LL TELLYA, I FIND THAT I DON'T NEED 'EM... Y'KNOW, WHAT WITH NOT EATIN' SO MUCH...
HERE, LEMME STRAIGHTEN OUT THIS FIRE FOR YA, ED...
BOB.

SURE. SAY, YA GOTTA *MATCH*, ED?
COAT POCKET. I...
TOXIC WASTE
to radio tranmissions, wind was blowing 190 south.
When radioactivity was found ... the plant, ... be leaking from ... to a "general

Y'KNOW, I...
EVERYTHING'S BLUE.
Y'KNOW...
EVERYTHING.
IT'S BLUE.

WRAP UP SOME RE-ED RO-SES FOR A BLU-U-UE LADEEE...
HEH HEH HEH.
Y'KNOW, I'DA NEVER LEFT BLOSSOMVILLE IF IT HADNA BIN FOR THE *TROUBLE...*
SSKRITCH
By Dan Duffey
Courier Staff Writer
HOUMA DA
WASHINGTON, Oct.
Nader accused the Administration
day of a "cruel cover-up," saying it had
failed to notify 200,000 workers of
health risks from toxic substances in
their jobs.

AFTER THE TROUBLE, THEY SENT AN *INVESTIGATOR*. NICE GUY. CALLED ED SOMETHIN'...
AFTER HIM THEY SENT *ANOTHER* INVESTIGATOR, AN' THEN THEY POURED A LOTTA *CEMENT* DOWN ON MY STASH IN THE PIT...

HEARD 'EM SAY THEY WERE *MOVIN'* THE DUMP DOWN HERE, TO *LOUISIANA*.
I FIGURED, Y'KNOW, I MIGHT AS WELL TAG ALONG...
Y'LIKE THIS *FIRE* I MADE, ED?

YEAH, I GUESS YOU DO.
S'A FUNNY THING... EVEN THOUGH I LEFT *BLOSSOMVILLE*, IT'S LIKE I TOOK PART OF IT *WITH* ME, Y'KNOW?
IT'S LIKE BLOSSOMVILLE'S *STILL HERE...*
The Morning
Deadly acid spill forces evacuation of 500 homes
Pinhole found at nuke site

"IN MY MIND, IN MY DREAMS...
"BLOSSOMVILLE'S STILL THERE IN MY DREAMS."
I WALK... THROUGH A BAD PLACE...
A BAD PLACE THAT I DO NOT KNOW...
I AM DREAMING.
BUT... WHOSE DREAM... AM I DREAMING?
AND WHERE... ARE ALL THE PEOPLE?
SOMETHING... HAPPENED... HERE.
SOMETHING BRIGHT AND AWFUL KISSED THE WORLD...
...AND LEFT... ITS SMEARED... BLUE... LIPSTICK-PRINT.
11

THE SOIL IS CURDLED... AND ALL THAT GROWS... GROWS WRONG.
IN A SKIN OF BLACK CINDER, PUDDLES REFLECT FIRE... RED AND WET AND GLISTENING-LIKE SORES...
THE SONG OF STILLBORN BIRDS ECHOES... THROUGH THE DEFORMED METAL TREES...
...THERE IS A RATTLE...
...IN THE THROAT...
...OF THE WIND...
...AND I AM ALONE.

ALONE IN DEATHTOWN.
PLEASE...
LET IT NOT HAVE HAPPENED YET...

LET THERE STILL BE GRASS.
IT WAS A DREAM.
THE KATYDIDS... CONTINUE... THEIR MONOTONOUS ACCUSALS... AND ABBY... IS SAFE... BESIDE ME.
IT WAS A DREAM... I CAN... FORGET IT... AND RETURN... TO SLEEP...
NO.
NO I CAN'T.
NUCLEAR WARNING
EDITORIAL PAGE
Easing toxic waste worries
YOUR OPINION
OUR OPINION

UP
Y'KNOW, I WAS DRINKIN' THIS STUFF FOR A COUPLA MONTHS 'FORE I FOUND OUT WHAT IT WAS.
"WASTE." THAT'S WHAT THEY CALL IT. WASTE FROM NUCULER FISHING. SUPPOSED T'BE BAD FOR YA.
ALPO DOG FOOD
THESE DAYS, EVERYTHIN'S SUPPOSED T'BE BAD FOR YA...
WHO CAN KEEP UP WITH ALL THAT HEALTH STUFF, ANYWAY? ALL THAT HIPPY ANTI-NUCULER STUFF...
I ASKYA, ED... WHADDA THEY EXPECT ME TO DO ABOUT IT?
GLUP LUP LUP!
RIGHT! THAT'S IT EXACTLY! THAT'S THE WORD! "COMMITTED"!
WE'RE COMMITTED TO NUCULER ENERGY. CAN'T PRETEND IT NEVER HAPPENED...
"NATURAL POWER"? FORGET IT! HOW YA GONNA RUN A CAR ON WINDMILLS AN' WATERWHEELS?
ANSWER ME THAT!
SEE? YOU CAN'T! WE NEED NUCULER FISHING!
...AN' THERE'S DEFENSE! A LOTTA THE JUNK COMES OUTTA THESE PLANTS MAKES MISSILES AN' STUFF...
CLOSE 'EM DOWN, WE'LL ALL END UP ON THE COLLECTIVE FARM SLUGGIN' BACK VODKA!
WE'RE COMMITTED, ED! COMMITTED AS AMERICAN CITIZENS!
I'M COMMITTED... YOU'RE COMMITTED... EVERYBODY'S COMMITTED!
SO WHY DON'T THEY ALL JUST SHUT UP ABOUT IT?
UP

BKKRANNG!
SSSHHH! KEEP THE NOISE DOWN FOR GODSAKES.
BLUB GURGLE

AAH, THERE AIN'T NOBODY ABOUT. NOT IN THIS SCUM-PIT...
MAYBE. HOW MANY MORE DRUMS OF THIS GARBAGE YOU GOT LEFT BACK THERE, ANYHOW?

OH, THIS IS THE LAST ONE...
FUB BLUP BUP

...FOR THE MOMENT.
PLLUSSH!

GOOD.
WHAT TIME'S THAT NERD MONROE ARRIVIN'?
TOMORROW, ROUND NOON. BRINGIN' HIS OL' LADY WITH HIM...

THE LITTLE FAT BROAD, ALWAYS TALKIN' 'BOUT JESUS? DIDN'T SHE HAVE A FUNNY NAME? WHAT THE HELL WAS THAT?
"TREASURE."
"TREASURE"! THAT'S RIGHT. HAHAHAHAHA...

BEATS ME HOW A WIMP LIKE MONROE ENDS UP WORKIN' FOR THE COMPANY AT ALL!
YEAH, WELL, AFTER FRANK GILL WENT A.W.O.L. BACK IN PENNSYLVANIA, I GUESS THEY HADDA SETTLE FOR WHAT THEY COULD GET...
SSHLUCC

DON'T TALK TO ME ABOUT PENNSYLVANIA, MAN. THAT PLACE GAVE ME THE CREEPS...
YEAH? AN' THIS PLACE DON'T?

WELL, Y'KNOW, AT LEAST THIS PLACE LOOKS HEALTHY.
HEY, THAT BOG WE DUMPED THE CANS IN... IT'S PRETTY DEEP, RIGHT?

DEEP ENOUGH.
IT'S LIKE THEY SAY: OUTTA SIGHT IS OUTTA MIND...

"...AN' WHAT THE EYE DON'T SEE...

"...THE HEART DON'T GRIEVE OVER."

Uranium Shipme

By RICHARD BERNSTEIN
Special to The New York Times

PARIS, Aug. 26 — A French cargo ship that sank off the coast of Belgium Saturday night was carrying containers filled with a form of uranium used to make fuel for nuclear reactors, the ship's owner and French Government officials said tonight.

Guy Lengagne, the Secretary of State for Maritime Affairs, said in a

DADA DA
LADA DA
DA DA...

DADA DA LADA DA
DA DA.

DADA DA LADA DA
DA DA...
PLUP
PLUP!

PENNSYLVANIA
SIX-FIVE-OH-OH-
OH!
HEH
HEH...
NO
DUMPING

HERE?

THEY DUMPED IT HERE...
THEY BURIED IT UNDER THE MUD!!
AWW, NO...
THEY GOT NO RIGHT! NO RIGHT TO BURY IT.
I'M ENTITLED! I'M AN AMERICAN CITIZEN...
AW, NO. WHADDAMI GONNA DO?
DIG IT UP. GOTTA DIG IT UP...
I'M ENTITLED. I...
WHUH?
ED? THAT YOU?
YA GOTTA HELP ME, BUDDY...
THEY BURIED IT.
THEY BURIED IT UNNA THE MUD!

WHAT... ARE... YOU?
ME?
I'M AN AMERICAN CITIZEN.
LISTEN, ED, WE GOTTA STICK TOGETHER. YA GOTTA HELP ME DIG IT UP...
YOU'RE LIKE ME, ED...
YOU'RE COMMITTED.
AAAUUUAAAAA
HHHNUH...
SSSSSSSSSSSSSSS

ED?
WHASSAMATTER, ED?
ONE OVER THE EIGHT! HUH?
LEMME HELPYA UP...
SSSSSSSIZZLE POP
UUUAAAEEEEIIGHH
S'NO GOOD... TOO HEAVY...
MAYBE WE BOTH BETTER REST... GET OUR STRENGTH BACK 'FORE WE DIG UP THE STASH...
...UUUGHH...
JA-LUP!
HMM
NOT MUCH LEFT NOW...
AW, HELL...
WHAT'RE FRIENDS FOR?
SAY, ED? I GOT SOMETHIN' FOR YA...

"OVER THE TEETH AN' ROUNNA GUMS, LOOK OUT STUMMICK...
"...HERE IT COMES!"
THERE...
GA-GURGLE!
IIIIUUGGHH
THERE'S GLORY FOR YA, HUH?
NOW, YOU JUST SIT BACK A WHILE, ED...
...AN' LEMME TELLYA 'BOUT PENNSYLVANIA...
...to be concluded...

CHAPTER FIVE
THE NUKEFACE PAPERS

Part Two

Created by:
LEN WEIN &
BERNI WRIGHTSON

EVENTUALLY... THE POISONOUS CREATURE LEAVES... TO SEARCH FOR MORE... OF THE EFFLUENT... THAT SUSTAINS HIM...
I DO NOT... SEE HIM... AGAIN...
I CANNOT LIFT MY HEAD... FAR ENOUGH... TO SEE THE GRADUALLY DEEPENING HOLE... IN MY CHEST...
BUT I CAN FEEL IT...
A COLD ACHE... SURROUNDED BY BLUE NUMBNESS...
THROUGHOUT... THE LONG... PARALYZED NIGHT... MY MIND IS CAUGHT... IN A GAUZE... OF DELERIUM...
I SEE A LANDSCAPE... WHOSE HARD EDGES... HAVE ERODED... INTO NEW... AND DISTURBING FORMS...
I THINK OF ABBY...
I LEFT HER SLEEPING... WHEN I CAME HERE... TO THIS PLACE... OF MY DESTRUCTION.
INSIDE MY MIND... I CALL HER NAME...
SHE DOES NOT ANSWER.
SHE DOES NOT... COME TO FIND ME...
ALL NIGHT I AM AWAKE... INSIDE THE ROTTING PRISON... OF MY BODY...
WITH THE FIRST LIGHT OF DAWN...
...I NOTICE...
...THAT MY ARM HAS GONE.

THE DAY PASSES SLOWLY...
DURING THE AFTERNOON... A HOLE APPEARS... IN MY STOMACH.
SOON... MY LOWER HALF... WILL BE DETACHED...
AS IT STARTS TO DECAY... MY HEAD FILLS... WITH ICE-BLUE NOTHINGNESS.
MY CONSCIOUSNESS... IS NOT CENTERED... IN MY BRAIN... AND I COULD SURVIVE... FOR A WHILE... WITHOUT A HEAD...
...BUT AFTER THAT...?
FEAR WELLS UP INSIDE ME... AND AGAIN... I CALL... MY LOVER'S NAME...
THERE IS A BRIEF PICTURE... ABBY AT ELYSIUM LAWNS... A CHILD SHOWING HER HIS PICTURE OF SANTA CLAUS... ALMOST TOO PROUD TO SPEAK...
THE IMAGE DISSOLVES... MELTING INTO THE BLUE SILENCE... THAT ENGULFS ME...
DID I MAKE CONTACT? DID ABBY HEAR ME?
AS DUSK FALLS... I BECOME BLIND... IN ONE EYE...
IN THE DISTANCE I HEAR SOMEONE... A MAN... CRASHING THROUGH THE TWILIGHT...
HE SHOUTS..."WHY DON'T YOU LEAVE ME ALONE?"... HIS VOICE FRIGHTENED.
SOON... I HEAR HIM... STUMBLING AWAY...
LATER... I IMAGINE I HEAR A WOMAN... PRAYING... VERY SOFTLY...
LATER STILL... THE SOUND OF MANY PEOPLE... CALLING TO EACH OTHER...
I NO LONGER EXIST FROM THE WAIST DOWN.

AND EVENTUALLY... SHE FINDS ME...
AAA... BY...?
DON'T... COME...CUH... CLOSER...
POISON...
OH GOD.
OH GOD, YOU'RE STILL ALIVE...
BODY DYING... ALL GONE SOON...
LISTEN... CUH... CAREFULLY...
CAN'T TALK...MUCH LONGER...
AND THEN I TELL HER...WHAT I PLAN TO DO...
...AND THEN...MY LOWER JAW... FALLS OFF...
...AND... AFTER A WHILE...
...I DIE...

OFFICER BERNHARDT:
...SO, LIKE, I DUNNO WHAT WENT DOWN FOR CERTAIN.
FIRST I HEARD OF IT WAS WIDOW MOREL TELLIN' ME HOW DIAGONAL BOB HAD DISAPPEARED...
"SEEMS THEY'D ARGUED, THE NIGHT BEFORE. SHE SLUNG BOB OUT, NEVER SAW HIM AGAIN... LEAST, NOT TILL SHE IDENTIFIED HIM THIS MORNIN', BUT THAT WAS LATER...
TIME SA
SALE
.65
SELF-SERVE GAS FOOD MAGAZINES
FRESH
69¢ PER POUND
VITAMIN D MILK
MILK
"WHILE SHE'S BENDIN' MY EAR, THIS MONROE GUY ARRIVES...
"HE'D OVERHEARD WIDOW MOREL'S STORY, AN' IT SEEMED TO UPSET HIM. I ASKED WHY AN' HE SAID SOMETHIN' ABOUT WINOS GOIN' MISSIN' IN PENNSYLVANIA, THEN WALKED OFF...
"LATER, I HEARD HE'D SCARED SOME NEIGHBORHOOD KIDS...
"ANYWAY, HE SEEMED PRETTY WEIRD.
TERRE BONNE PARISH
"WHEN HE TURNED UP AT THE STATION, LATER ON, WITH THAT STORY... HOW SOME MONSTER HAD GOT HIS WIFE AN' WE HADDA FIND HER... I THOUGHT, Y'KNOW, 'UH-OH!'
"BUT THEN SHE TURNED UP... AND THEN LATER WE FOUND BOB..."
...AND NOW I DUNNO WHAT TO THINK.
SAY!
WHO DEALT THIS MESS?
Satell
watch o
nuclear
cargo

WALLACE MONROE:
"TREASURE... PLEASE...
"PLEASE DON'T LOOK AT ME LIKE THAT.
"I WANT TO HOLD YOU. I WANT TO MAKE EVERYTHING ALL RIGHT, BUT MY LEGS WON'T LET ME. THEY JUST KEEP BACKING AWAY FROM YOU...
"BACKING AWAY ACROSS THE WET MORNING GRASS...
"REMEMBER YESTERDAY MORNING, WHEN WE ARRIVED HERE FROM PENNSYLVANIA AFTER DRIVING OVERNIGHT? YOU WERE HOT AND UNCOMFORTABLE. THE BABY WAS KICKING...
"WE STOPPED FOR MILK. OUTSIDE THE STORE, A WOMAN WAS TALKING TO A COP..."
OKAY! SO WE ARGUED! SO I WAS ACCIDENTALLY HOLDING MY NAIL FILE WHEN I SHOVED THE BUM.
LISTEN... YOU DON'T CARE! HE'S JUST SOME WINO, RIGHT? BUT HE'S GONE MISSIN'! WHAT ABOUT MY BACK RENT?
"IT COULDN'T BE. DERELICTS HAD GONE MISSING IN PENNSYLVANIA, BUT I'D PUT THAT NIGHT-MARE BEHIND ME. THE COMPANY CLOSED THE DUMP AND MOVED US HERE..."
EXCUSE ME...?
DID YOU SAY... A DRUNKARD WAS MISSING?
"I WAS STUPID TO SPEAK LIKE THAT. IT JUST MADE THE COP SUSPICIOUS.
"I WALKED BACK TO THE CAR AND TOLD YOU I'D BEEN ASKING DIRECTIONS, AND YOU BELIEVED ME BECAUSE YOU ALWAYS BELIEVE ME.

"WE DROVE ON AND CHECKED IN TO OUR MOTEL, AND I WENT OUT TO BUY A NEWSPAPER.
"ON THE WAY BACK I SAW SOME CHILDREN PLAYING IN A VACANT LOT. THEY WERE CHANTING SOMETHING..."
NUKEFACE
NUKEFACE
NUKEFACE
"WHERE? WHERE HAD THEY GOT THAT NAME FROM? THAT'S WHAT THE CHILDREN IN PENNSYL-VANIA HAD CHANTED... BUT THAT WAS HUNDREDS OF MILES AWAY!
"I SHOUTED AT THEM AND MADE A COMPLETE FOOL OF MYSELF.
"BACK AT THE MOTEL I JUST PACED AROUND OR SAT STARING. I MUST HAVE LOOKED CRAZY.
"WAS THERE SOMETHING? SOMETHING THAT CAME OUT OF THE DUMPS IN PENNSYLVANIA AND KILLED DERELICTS? SOMETHING THAT HAD FOLLOWED US HERE?
"NUKEFACE.
"DUSK WAS FALLING. I TOLD YOU I NEEDED TO GO FOR A WALK AND YOU SAID TO GET SOME MORE MILK ON THE WAY BACK.
hour is considered a significant radiation dose. In comparison, the highest exposure a bystander could have received from the nuclear accident at Three Mile Island was 100 millirads, or about one-tenth of a rad.
A rad is a unit of absorbed radiation. An average chest X-ray produces 20 to 30 millirads instantaneously. A lethal dose for half the population is 450 rads received instantaneously over the whole body.
"If you sat next to a pellet over many hours, you might several days later develop a reddening of the
"I KNEW HE WAS OUT THERE, AND THAT SOMEHOW IT WAS THE COMPANY'S FAULT... MY FAULT, EVEN. I HAD TO FIND HIM. I HAD TO DO SOMETHING...
"FOR SOME REASON, I DECIDED TO SEARCH THE SWAMPS.

"I GOT LOST.
"I WANDERED AROUND FOR HOURS, GROWING MORE FRIGHTENED AND DESPERATE WITH EACH CRACK OF A BRANCH OR NEARBY SCRABBLING.
"AT ONE POINT, I BECAME CONVINCED THAT SOMETHING LURKED NEARBY, LISTENING TO MY EVERY BREATH.
"I YELLED AT THE EMPTY SHADOWS..."
WHY DON'T YOU LEAVE ME ALONE!!
"THERE WAS NO REPLY. I CRASHED THROUGH THE UNDERGROWTH AND EVENTUALLY FOUND MY WAY OUT ONTO A ROAD.
"IT TOOK ME ANOTHER HOUR TO LOCATE OUR MOTEL. I'D FORGOTTEN THE STREET NAME.
LA 3197
"AND WHEN I FOUND IT... YOU WEREN'T THERE...
8:30: Gone to look for you and buy milk. If you get home, stay put. Treasure xxx
"THE NOTE SAID EIGHT THIRTY. TWO HOURS BEFORE.

"MY STOMACH FELT LIKE LEAD. YOU WERE PREGNANT, OUT ON YOUR OWN IN A STRANGE NEIGHBORHOOD...
"...AND THERE WAS A MONSTER OUT THERE.
"I NEVER TOLD YOU EXACTLY WHAT THE COMPANY DID. I'D BEEN COVERING UP... FOR THE COMPANY AND FOR MYSELF. COVERING UP HAD LED ME TO THIS.
"WHEN I REACHED THE POLICE STATION, I WAS RAVING.

"I BABBLED TO THE OFFICER I'D MET EARLIER, ABOUT DERELICTS, KIDS, NUCLEAR WASTE, MONSTERS... HE DIDN'T BELIEVE ME.
"FINALLY, I TOLD HIM YOU WERE PREGNANT, AND HE AGREED TO ORGANIZE A SEARCH PARTY.
SHERIFF
SHERIFF
"WE TRUDGED THROUGH THE DARK SWAMPS, CALLING OUT TO EACH OTHER.
"ONE OF THE MEN FOUND SOME PATCHES OF GRASS, LUMINOUS AND CONTAMINATED, AND AFTER THAT THEY DIDN'T LAUGH AT MY STORY SO MUCH...
"...BUT WE DIDN'T FIND YOU. WE SEARCHED UNTIL THE NEXT MORNING, AND THEN FINALLY, WHEN I'D GIVEN UP HOPE...
"...YOU WANDERED OUT OF NOWHERE AND FOUND US.
"JUST FOR A MOMENT I WAS SO HAPPY...
"AND THEN I ASKED YOU WHERE YOU'D BEEN...
"...AND YOU TOLD ME.
Nuclear Spill Among the Worst
"TREASURE... PLEASE...
"PLEASE DON'T LOOK AT ME LIKE THAT.
"I CAN NO LONGER BEAR THE SIGHT OF YOUR EYES.
"I TURN, AND I BEGIN TO RUN...
"...KNOWING ALREADY THAT I SHALL NEVER STOP."

MRS. MOREL:
HOLY MOTHER.
YES, THAT'S HIM.
OH GOD, COVER HIM UP, HE'S A TERRIBLE SIGHT...

WHAT'S HE IN A *BAG* FOR, ANYWAY? IT'S NOT AS IF HE HAD ANY *AILMENTS* OR *DISEASES!*
I ALWAYS *INSISTED* HE KEPT HIMSELF *CLEAN*. I KEEP A *VERY CLEAN* HOUSE, AN' YOU CAN ASK *ANYONE*...
100
105
COWS

ASK *ME*, IT'S THAT FELLA FROM *PENNSYLVANIA* AT THE BOTTOM OF THIS. DID YOU *HEAR?* HE RAN OFF AN' LEFT HIS *WIFE!* POOR GIRL'S IN *HOSPITAL* NOW...
I SUSPECTED HIM FROM THE START...
99
WE ARE NOT COWS

FIRST THAT BOTHER OUTSIDE THE *STORE*, THEN THAT BUSINESS WITH *BILLY HATCHER*...
NOW MY *BOB'S* GONE. ALTHOUGH, YOU UNDERSTAND, HE WAS JUST MY *TENANT*. A *PAYING* TENANT... WHAT-EVER THOSE OLD SPINSTERS SAY...
HE OWED *BACK RENT*...

OH GOD.
I THREW HIM OUT...
'It's O.K.—We're Still Alive
Mr. Sotelo, who has three children, said that he has been dismissed from his job and cannot find another, and that his neighbors are worried and upset. But "It's O.K.," he said. "We're still alive. Maybe the doctors exaggerated the danger."
10

TREASURE MONROE:
"WALLACE?
"WHAT HAVE I DONE WRONG?
"WHY ARE YOU WALKING AWAY FROM ME?
"PLEASE, WALLACE...
"WHAT'S HAPPENED TO US?
"YOU'VE ACTED SO STRANGE SINCE WE ARRIVED IN LOUISIANA. AFTER ASKING THOSE PEOPLE AT THE STORE FOR DIRECTIONS, YOU BARELY SPOKE TO ME.
TIME
SAVER
SERV
"AND THEN AT THE MOTEL, ESPECIALLY AFTER YOU WENT OUT FOR THAT NEWSPAPER.
"WHEN YOU SAID YOU WERE GOING FOR A WALK, I WAS RELIEVED. I THOUGHT IT MIGHT RELAX YOU.
22
"I'D ASKED YOU TO BUY MILK. AN HOUR WENT BY AND YOU WEREN'T BACK AND I WAS THIRSTY. I WENT TO THE STORE, THEN WENT TO LOOK FOR YOU...
"THE SWAMPS LOOKED BEAUTIFUL AT DUSK.
11

"I GUESS IT WAS STUPID OF ME TO LOOK FOR YOU IN THERE. I'VE NEVER HAD ANY SENSE OF DIRECTION.
"I GOT LOST.
"I DIDN'T MIND BEING LOST... IT WAS SUCH A BEAUTIFUL NIGHT. I JUST DIDN'T WANT YOU TO BE WORRIED.
MILK
Boudreau Dairy
MILK
SO GOOD FOR YOU!
"I DECIDED TO DRINK HALF THE MILK, AND THEN SEARCH AGAIN FOR A WAY OUT.
"THAT WAS WHEN I FOUND HIM.
OPAL, India (AP) – The
rnment radio said Thursday
1,600 people died from a cloud
poison gas, and doctors said the
were getting cases in which deadly
umes killed children in the womb.
Smoke from mass cremations
over the stricken city and
News of India said the death
pesticide plant had already
ore than 2,000.
were eight stillbirths,
Doctors also were quoted as say
ing they had to perform an unspec
fied number of abortions on preg
nant women who had been expos
to the gas, and were brought to
hospital in terrible pain.
"I WAS SO STARTLED THAT I DROPPED THE MILK. I REMEMBER THINKING 'OH WELL, IT'S NO USE CRYING OVER SPILLED MILK.' ISN'T THAT SILLY?
"THAT POOR MAN. HE WAS SO SICK...
"I DIDN'T KNOW WHAT TO DO, THEN I SAID 'WELL, WHAT WOULD JESUS CHRIST HAVE DONE?'
"THERE WAS NO QUESTION.
"I PUT MY COAT OVER HIM, THEN LAID DOWN AND TRIED TO KEEP HIM WARM.
MILK
"HE HAD A SKIN DISEASE... HIS SKIN GLOWED. I HEAR PEOPLE WHO WORKED IN MATCH FACTORIES SUFFER THE SAME COMPLAINT. HE WAS SO UGLY.
"BUT THAT'S WHAT CHRIST TAUGHT, ISN'T IT? TO LOVE THE UNLOVABLE?

"BEFORE I WENT TO SLEEP, I SAID A PRAYER FOR HIM, OUT LOUD.
"WHEN I AWOKE IN THE MORNING I LISTENED FOR A HEARTBEAT, BUT I'M CERTAIN HE WAS DEAD.

"IN DAYLIGHT, IT WAS EASY TO FIND MY WAY OUT OF THE SWAMP.
"I RAN STRAIGHT INTO YOU, AND ALL OF THESE POLICEMEN...

"YOU LOOKED SO HAPPY TO SEE ME, AND THEN YOU ASKED WHERE I'D BEEN...
"I TOLD YOU ABOUT THE TRAMP, AND IT WAS AS IF EVERYTHING TURNED COLD ALL OF A SUDDEN..."

Y-YOU LAY NEXT TO HIM? ALL NIGHT? AND HE WAS GLOWING?
YES... HE WAS ILL. WALLACE, WHAT'S WRONG?
OH JEEZ... THOSE FOOTPRINTS WE FOUND...

NOTHING. NOTHING'S WRONG.
YOU...YOU JUST STAY THERE, TREASURE. EVERYTHING'S OKAY. WE'LL FIND A DOCTOR...
DOCTOR? WALLACE... WALLACE, I DON'T UNDERSTAND...

WUH-WHAT'S WRONG WITH EVERYBODY? I HAVEN'T DONE ANYTHING.
WHY WON'T ANYBODY COME NUH-NEAR ME?

WALLACE?
WHAT HAVE I DONE WRONG??
nuclear official quits
FRITZ BUMPED
REAGAN'S LANDSLIDE VICTORY

BILLY HATCHER:
LISTEN, PAY NO ATTENTION TO WHAT EDDIE SAID. THAT GUY CAN BE A REAL HOMO AT TIMES.
THIS IS WHAT REALLY HAPPENED, AN' YOU CAN CUT MY BLEEDIN' HEART OUT IF I TELL A LIE...
18
Uranium Shipment
"FIRST THING YESTERDAY MORNING, RIGHT, I'D BEEN FISHIN' OUT IN THE SWAMPS, I SEES THIS GUY...
"HE'S A REAL MUTANT, Y'KNOW? ZITS, AND BITS O' STUFF FALLIN' OFF HIS FACE AN' EVERYTHIN'...
"I YELL 'NUKEFACE' AT HIM, 'CAUSE, LIKE, THAT WAS THE NAME I THOUGHT UP, AN' THEN I SPLIT.
"THAT'S WHAT GAVE ME THE IDEA FOR THIS MASK, SEE?
"ANYWAY, LATER, WHEN WE WAS PLAYIN'.. YOU WERE THERE, PINTO... THIS CRAZY GUY COMES UP AN' STARTS SHOUTIN' AT US.
"'THIS ISN'T PENNSYLVANIA! THOSE DUMPS WERE SAFE!' ALL KINDA CRAZY STUFF...
"WE BEAT IT."
LATER, MIKE BERNHARDT'S BROTHER TOLD ME THE REST...
THIS MONROE, THE CRAZY GUY, HE LEFT TOWN. IT'S BECAUSE HIS WIFE WENT OUT WITH NUKEFACE, Y'KNOW, IN THE WOODS, AN' NOW SHE'S GONNA HAVE A SCREWED-UP BABY!
THIS WOMAN, MONROE'S WIFE, WHO'S IN HOSPITAL NOW, SHE SAYS THAT WHEN SHE LEFT OL' NUKEFACE, THERE IN THE SWAMPS, HE WAS DEAD..
BUT JOEY BERNHARDT SAYS HIS BROTHER AIN'T FOUND THE BODY YET...
Uranium Shipment We
BERNSTEIN
ew York Times
A French carg
he coast of Belgium
as carrying contain-
s filled with a form of uranium used
make fuel for nuclear reactors, the
hip's owner and French Government
fficials said tonight.
An official in the French Ministry of
he Environment, Jean-Claude Roure,
aid an investigation carried out by
French maritime officials near the
wreck revealed "no trace of radioactivity in the area," indicating the containers had not broken during the colli-
sion.
collected fro
leakage."
The owne
Louis, which
near Ostend
carrying 450
ride, a mildl
is an interm
duction of r
used in the n
OFF AND RUN
...SO WHO KNOWS?
15

ABBY CABLE:
"I WAKE FROM CONFUSED DREAMS IN WHICH I HEAR YOU CALL MY NAME FROM FAR AWAY...
"BESIDE ME, THERE IS ONLY AN EMPTY SPACE AND THAT FAINT MOSS-FRAGRANCE THAT YOU LEAVE BEHIND YOU.
"YOU MUST HAVE GONE WALKING AT DAWN, NOT WANTING TO WAKE ME.
"I HAVE TO GO TO WORK.
"I OUGHT TO CHECK IN AT MY APARTMENT IN HOUMA, BUT I DON'T HAVE TIME, I TOLD DEANNA I'D BE AT THE HOME EARLY TODAY.
"I TAKE THE BUS, AND THINK ABOUT YOU.
"IT'S SO STRANGE, OUR LIFE TOGETHER. ME LIVING IN HOUMA DURING THE WEEK AND STAYING OUT AT THE SWAMPS WEEKENDS WITH YOU.
"I REALLY LIKE IT.
"DURING THE AFTERNOON, AT ELYSIUM LAWNS, TOMMY SHOWS ME ONE OF THE SCREEN-PRINT PICTURES HE'S HELPED WITH.
"TOMMY'S NON-VERBAL. HE STANDS THERE SMILING AND NODDING WHILE I LOOK AT THE PICTURE...
"...AND THEN ALL OF A SUDDEN SOMETHING FLASHES INSIDE MY HEAD...
"...AND I CAN SEE YOU!

"THE IMAGE VANISHES, AND TOMMY IS STARING AT ME, LOOKING UNHAPPY. HE THINKS HIS PICTURE UPSET ME.
"ALL THE REST OF THE DAY I WORRY, AND LEAVE A HALF-HOUR EARLY.
"I STOP AT MY APARTMENT, FOR A FLASHLIGHT, THEN HEAD STRAIGHT OUT TO THE SWAMPS. THAT'S WHERE I SAW YOU, IN THE VISION...
"I SEARCH FOR HOURS, WALKING MILES...
"SHORTLY, I HEAR SOME MEN CRASHING THROUGH THE WOODS, SHOUTING TO EACH OTHER, AND I STAND STILL UNTIL THEY PASS ON.
"AN HOUR LATER, I FIND YOU.
"IS IT YOU? BUT... THERE'S HARDLY ANYTHING LEFT... A TORSO, AN ARM, HALF A HEAD...
"IT'S NOT YOU. IT'S JUST... A MESS!
"AND THEN THE MESS OPENS ITS REMAINING EYE...
"...AND SPEAKS MY NAME."
AAA... BY...?
DON'T... COME... CUH... CLOSER...
POISON...

OH GOD.
OH GOD, YOU'RE STILL ALIVE...
PLUP
BODY DYING... ALL GONE SOON...
LISTEN... CUH... CAREFULLY...
CAN'T TALK... MUCH LONGER...
I'M GUH... GOING TO TRY... TO LEAVE MY BODY...
SEND... MY MIND... OUT INTO... THE GREEN...
I WAITED... FOR YOU... TO CUH... COME... SO I... COULD TELL YOU...
BUT... YOUR BODY! IT'S JUST FALLING APART! YOU WON'T HAVE A BODY TO COME BACK TO...
OH, ALEC, WHAT DID THIS TO YOU...?
NO TIME... TO EXPLAIN. YUH... YOU ARE... RIGHT...
THIS BUH... BODY WILL... DIE...
I'M GOING... TO TRY... TO BUILD... A NEW BODY...
IF... IT WORKS... I'LL SEE YOU... SUH... SOON...
IF... IT DOESN'T...
I LOVE YOU, ABBY.

ALEC?
ALEC, SAY SOMETHING...
ARE YOU STILL THERE?
PLUP
"YOU DON'T ANSWER.

"I STAND THERE AMONGST THE MUTE AND HORRIFIED TREES, AND I WATCH YOU...

3-Mile Plant
May Reopen
19
"... UNTIL YOU'RE ALL GONE."

NUKEFACE:
GZUH?
PLIP!
OAW...
OAW, MY HEAD...
MUSTA BIN SOME KINDA PARTY...
WHAT THE HELL HAPPENED, ANYWAY? HUH?
I 'MEMBER, I'D JUST FOUND THAT BIG MUD-PUDDLE WHERE...
...WHERE THEY'D BURIED...
"AW NO. I REMEMBER...
"THEY'D BURIED THE STUFF! BURIED IT UNDER THE MUD WHERE I COULDN'T GET TO IT!
"AW, GODDAMMIT...
"AN'.. AN' THERE WAS THAT GUY! ED WHATZISNAME...
"HE WAS GONNA HELP ME DIG IT UP, BUT THEN HE JUST LAY THERE...
"THAT BIG BASTUD... AFTER I GIVE HIM MY LAST SHOT O' JUICE!

"I COULD SEE HE WEREN'T GONNA BE NO HELP, SO I WENT OFF TO LOOK FOR THE STUFF SOMEPLACE ELSE...
"DIDN'T FIND NONE.
"OH YEAH... AN' AS IF I DIDN'T GOT ENOUGH TROUBLE, I GET SOME ROTTEN LITTLE KID SHOUTIN' AT ME, LIKE THEY USED TO DO BACK IN PENNSYLVANIA...
"WHO NEEDS IT?
"BOY, I WAS HURTIN' SOMETHIN' AWFUL...
"NEEDED A TASTE SO BAD, IT WAS CHEWIN' UP MY INSIDES. MAN, I TELLYA, ONE DAY I'M GONNA QUIT THIS STUFF...
"I MUSTA WANDERED ROUND ALL DAY, THE PAIN JUST GETTIN' WORSE... THEN I GUESS I COLLAPSED...
"WHAT HAPPENED THEN?
"IT WAS FUNNY... SOMETIMES I KNEW I WAS IN THE SWAMP THERE, BUT SOMETIMES I THOUGHT I WAS BACK IN BLOSSOMVILLE...
"I WAS IN THE SHANTY TOWN OUT THERE, AN'... JEEZ! I JUST REMEMBERED! THEY WERE ALL THERE! ALL MY OLD DRINKIN' BUDDIES WERE THERE!
"...BUT NONE OF 'EM WOULD TALK TO ME.
WE ARE NOT COWS
13
"FUNNY...

"AND... AN' I DREAMED ABOUT A WOMAN...
"SHE WAS LIKE... LIKE MY MOM. SHE COVERED ME UP, AND SHE HUGGED ME, AND SHE SAID A PRAYER FOR ME..."
GEE...
GEE, THAT WAS, Y'KNOW...
THAT WAS A NICE DREAM.
SNIFF
WELL, NO SENSE SITTIN' ROUND MOPIN'. GOTTA FIND ME SOME MORE STASH. THERE'S GOTTA BE SOME MORE OF IT OUT THERE SOMEPLACE... LOTS OF IT...
HELL, I CAN SMELL IT! JUST NEEDS PERSEVERANCE AN' DETERMINATION...
PLUP!
DON'T CARE IF I GOTTA LOOK IN EVERY STATE, EVERY TOWN... EVERY STREET, DAMMIT!
IT'S THERE, BOY. I KNOW IT'S THERE...
PERSEVERANCE AN' DETERMINATION, THAT'S ALL IT TAKES...

HEADS UP, AMERICA...

was worse than thought

MIDDLETOWN, Pa. — The core of Three Mile Island's Unit 2 reactor came closer to melting down than previously estimated during the 1979 accident, a study released Tuesday reported. The new study, done by EG&G, Inc. for the federal government, said temperatures in the core reached at least 4,800 degrees, only 280 degrees short of meltdown and the surface of some uranium began to melt. Previous studies put the temperature at 3,500 degrees. The Nuclear Regulatory Commission on Tuesday is deciding whether to force complete upgrading of an emergency system at Three Mile Island's undamaged reactor before allowing it to restart, possibly next year.

Hazardous-Waste

two of their hired hands, and they're all buried here in Parowan cemetery. The only one left from those farms is Earl Bunn, and now he's got cancer of the spine and prostate.

Glenna Orton, Parowan, Utah

Well, just within a block of my home there's Wilford, he had cancer, and his wife Helen died of stomach cancer. Carl across the street died of throat cancer, and Ernie died of it, and his wife has it now. The boy next to them died of leukemia, and my sister across the way there, she died. And her husband has it now....

Irma Thomas, St. George, Utah

Verla's dad, and Paul Stewart, and Dan Potter, and my husband Kent...

Jane Bradshaw, Hiko, Nev.

... two of my brothers, my father, and my son...

Irene Bistline, Colorado City, Ariz.

... my father, my brother-in-law, my son, and my husband...

Lois Blood, Cedar City, Utah

... my sister, my niece, my aunt, four uncles, my sister-in-law, my mother-in-law, my grandmother, and my wife...

Elmer Pickett, St. George, Utah

... two of my aunts. Three of my uncles. And two of my doctors.

Dave Timothy, St. George, Utah

First you'd see a flash of light, it'd light this whole house up. Then you'd hear the blast, and then you'd see the mushroom. It was really something. We used to let the kids out in their swimsuits to see it.

Roma Lundberg, St. George, Utah

The ones who died got off easy. It's the ones who lived that have it hard.

Vonda McKinney, Holbrook, Ariz.

NO ILLNESS FOUND IN DIOXIN TESTING

I was a teacher in Panguitch in '51 when the blasting started. One day after a blast it was my turn to take my phys ed class out on the field, and I didn't want to because I'd read about Hiroshima. But the principal told me I had to. Later he died of cancer. So did three of my students. So did the other phys ed teacher.

St. George, Utah

KIRKWOOD, Mo., Oct. 17 (AP) — Tests on people exposed to dioxin in eastern Missouri showed no "meaningful ill-health effects," health officials say, but many residents are still skeptical.

When our daughter Sybil D. contracted leukemia, I asked the doctor up in charge of the hematology clinic in Salt Lake, wasn't it a little bit more than a coincidence that there should be seven cases of leukemia within a hundred yards of our house?

Blaine Johnson, Cedar City, Utah

Worker at Nuclear Plant ... ed by Water Burst

The flashes would come early in the morning when I was teaching in the old two-room schoolhouse. The children would come in and say, "Mrs. Kelsey! Mrs. Kelsey! Did you see that flash this morning? Did you see it?"

Viola Kelsey, New Harmony, Utah

My father and I were both morticians, and when these cancer cases started coming in I had to go into my books to study how to do the embalming, cancers were so rare. In '56 and '57 all of a sudden they were coming in all the time. By 1960 it was a regular flood.

Elmer Pickett, St. George, Utah

'Cruel Cover-Up' on Job Poisons

B. TOTLEBEN
9.20.84